THE WONDERS OF THE
RED SEA

TEXT:
DAVID FRIDMAN
PHOTOS & ILLUSTRATIONS:
TONY MALMQVIST

Surrounded by a huge desert region, the Red Sea extension is approximately 2000 km (1300 miles) from the northern tip, the Bay of Eilat- Aqaba, to the Bab Al Mandeb Straits, in the south. The Gulf of Aqaba is in the northern part, 180 km (110 miles), from the Tiran Straits. With a maximum width of 25 km (14 miles), this narrow body of water attains depths of up to 1800 m (6000 feet), due it's being part of the Syrian-African Rift Valley, extending throughout the Red Sea all the way to the south with fringing reefs. This gulf is very special in many aspects: Water temperature is relatively constant, without major changes: in summer up to 25

The Red Sea

/26° and in winter not less than 21/22°. No big storms (except occasionally in the winter), mild currents and the lack of rain do not bring much sediment from land. All these elements ensure excellent clarity of the water and a rich variety of coral growth. The very low humidity in the air and the high rate of evaporation due to the heat in the area make the Red Sea one of the saltiest life-sustaining seas in the world. Salinity reaches up to 4.1% and has isolated and developed a large variety of species endemic to the area. As a result this area has one of the richest concentrations of varieties of marine life in all of the tropical seas.

INTRODUCTION

Throughout the history of the region, the Red Sea has always had a magical attraction to man. The different aspects of studies in geology, paleontology, archaeology, religion etc. have given humans a continuous interest throughout the ages. In modern times, however, with the advance of technology, the focus on learning about the incredible, unique and rich marine life attracts numerous scientists (marine biologists) to study the highly interesting and amazing life under the surface of the water. Divers, underwater photographers, sea-life enthusiasts, all have contributed to broadening the knowledge about the huge variety of marine life.

Geographically situated in the Indo-Pacific- tropical seas region has allowed the Red Sea to develop a rich population of fishes and invertebrates (corals, sponges, sea anemones, urchins, sea stars, etc.) that are typical to the whole region. An entirely separate population, however, that is found only in the Red Sea, called "endemic", is not less than 10% of the total described life.

From the mid-19th century to this day, approximately 1000 species of fishes have been classified, most of them belonging to the popula-tion of the coral reefs which are famous also for their richness in other varieties of sea creatures. The purpose of this small book is to introduce to the reader part of this marine life, through drawings and underwater photographs, thus contributing to the existing knowledge and information about some of the most interesting, unusual, colorful and unique fishes in general and special coral fishes, as well as some representatives of the invertebrate kingdom, such as corals (both hard and soft, sponges, sea anemones, equinoderms (sea stars, cucumbers, urchins), crustaceans (crabs, lobsters, shrimps), and mollusks (shells, snails, nudibranches, squids and octopus).

It is important to remark that all of the drawings and underwater photographs are the result of the patient and dedicated artistic work of Tony Malmqvist who has devoted many years to his love for the sea and this area in particular. In the marine life population, we cannot forget to include two important groups of animals which contribute to the amazing varieties and to the food chain of this area. These are:
(1) Marine mammals (THE DOLPHINS) and
(2) Marine reptiles (SEA TURTLES)

FRINGING REEFS STRAIGHT FROM SHORE - IDEAL FOR SCUBA AND SNORKELDIVERS

THE KINGDOM OF THE CORAL REEFS

PLANKTON-LIFE IN THE WATER BODY BEGINS THE FOOD CHAIN

Millions of marine creatures live in a complex ecosystem where a very fragile equilibrium maintains all these animals in a necessary co-existence, as part of the chain which creates the coral reefs and their surroundings. From almost invisible life-forms to huge fish or mammals, all are equally important and contribute to the food chain, thus creating the conditions for the building and the healthy state of the coral reef. *TO PROTECT THIS DELICATE ENVIRONMENT FROM HUMAN POLLUTION, WE MUST SHOW CONCERN AND BE CARING RESIDENTS OF THIS PLANET.*

We will present here a few of the life-forms which help create the coral reef.

FEATHER WORMS IN THE REEF

TUBE SPONGE, ONE OF THE MANY VARIETIES OF THE REEF

SARQASSUM ALGEA GROWING ON THE SEA FLOOR

JELLYFISH SWIMMING WITH THE CURRENT

STONY FINGER CORALS BUILDING THE REEFS

COLOURFUL SOFT CORALS - RICHNESS OF THE CORAL REEFS

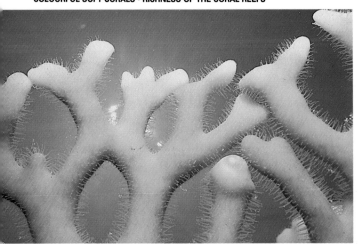

FIRE CORAL - A COMMON DWELLER OF THE SHALLOWS

FAN CORALS ARE COMMON IN DEEPER WATERS

7

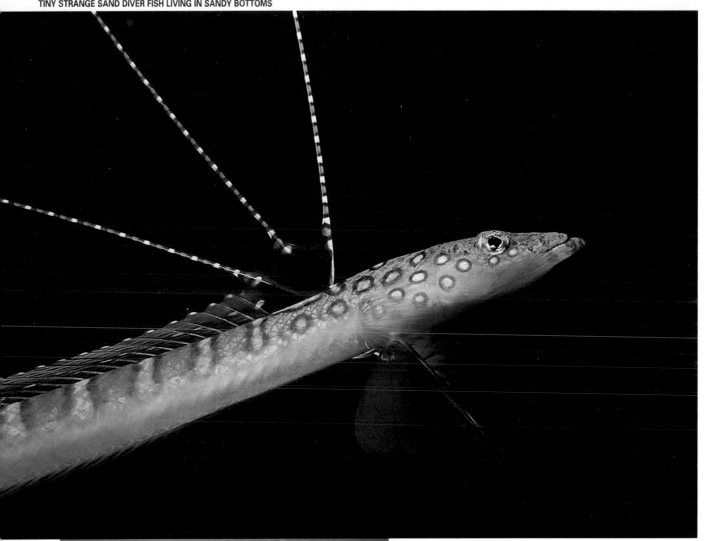

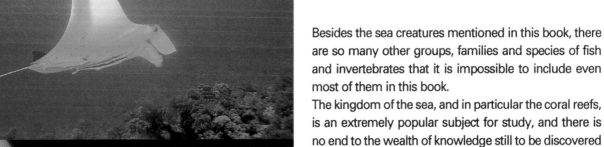

MANTA RAY - GIANT OF THE OPEN WATER FISHES

Besides the sea creatures mentioned in this book, there are so many other groups, families and species of fish and invertebrates that it is impossible to include even most of them in this book.

The kingdom of the sea, and in particular the coral reefs, is an extremely popular subject for study, and there is no end to the wealth of knowledge still to be discovered about this magnificent world. New species are being constantly revealed and the fragile, balanced, complex form of life is greatly admired. There still remains a huge amount of material for future generations to study in the kingdom of marine life.

SHARKS ARE IMPORTANT IN THE FOODCHAIN CONTROL

SYMBIOTIC LIFE BETWEEN THE CLOWN FISH AND THE SEA ANEMONE

THE TRITON - MAJESTIC SNAIL OF THE TROPICS

BANDED CORAL SHRIMPS, CLEANERS OF THE REEF FISH

SEA STAR WITH ATTRACTIVE COLOURS

SEA TURTLE - ENDANGERED REPTILE OF THE SEAS

9

FEATHER STAR *(SEA LILY)* **WITH NOCTURNAL ACTIVITY**

THE NEEDS OF A CORAL REEF

It is well known that 75% of the earth's surface is covered by water in a mass inter-connected system called "oceans". Our planet is richly supplied with water, and the seas are filled with life-forms, from the eternally dark abyssal depths to the abundantly lighted shallows. The shallows naturally developed the richness of life as a result of the energy provided by the light. Energy creates life.

We know that life on land is restricted to the earth's surface, while in the oceans it extends to all three dimensions. The open water is populated by a multiple of organisms which spend their entire lives swimming or floating in the water body. All life in the seas is adapted to the varied climatic and geographical conditions of the water, creating a diversity according to the nature of the area of the globe in which it is found.

In this chapter, we limit our dedication to the tropical seas and the coral reefs that are found in different areas of the continent. Of the varied habitats, the coral reefs stand out by their richness of species and diversity of life-forms. Unique and special conditions are required for the formation of the coral reefs. These range from the water temperatures, currents, water clarity, sediments washed down from land, richness of plankton, topography of the sea floor at different depths, water salinity and many other elements.

Altogether these factors determine the richness of these rocky formations created over hundreds of thousands or millions of years by a delicate, small creature called the coral polyp.

The best conditions for typical coral reefs are tropical, warm seas where the water temperature doesn't vary with the seasons. Ideal water temperature should not be lower than 20 degrees centigrade and not higher than 30.

In areas where land activity and sediment build-up are minimal, the water is clear, allowing penetration of light which is so important to the growth of the coral.

The diversity and intensity of the currents which bring either a weak or strong circulation of water and plankton, as well as the various types of topography of the sea floor, create a variety of forms of coral reefs.
The three main categories are described below.

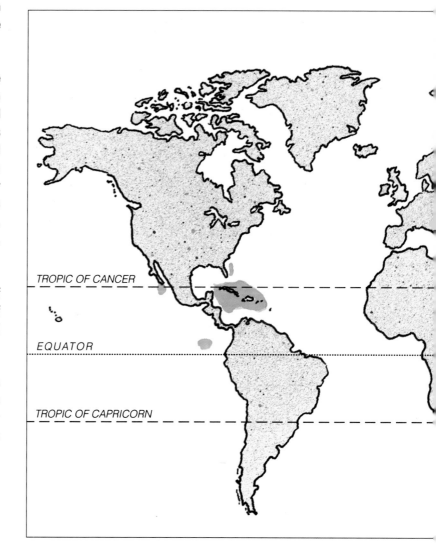

TROPIC OF CANCER

EQUATOR

TROPIC OF CAPRICORN

FRINGING REEFS
Grow outward from the coast with drop-offs close to shore like those in the Gulf of Aqaba and the Red Sea.

BARRIER REEFS
Huge coral reef formations separated from the coast by a lagoon like the Australian Barrier Reef.

ATOLL REEFS
Grow around submerged islands, mainly in the remote open ocean areas like the South Pacific.

GIANT SEA FAN IN THE DEEP REEFS

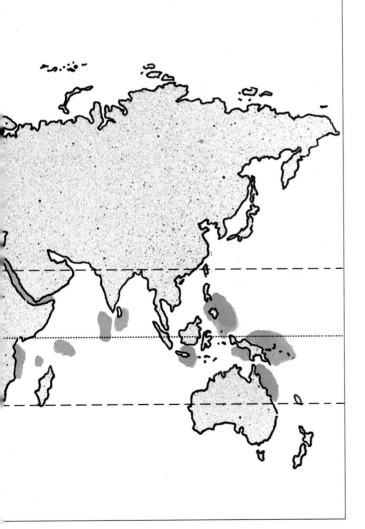

Map showing proliferation of coral reefs in different areas of tropical seas in the world, mostly south of the Tropic of Cancer and north of the Tropic of Capricorn. (The northern Red Sea is an exception)

11

THE CORAL POLYP

CLOSE-UP OF OPEN POLYPS OF A CUP CORAL *(TUBASTREA)*

The architects and builders of the coral reef formations are called coral polyps. These almost diminutive living creatures have tubular bodies with only one opening which is surrounded by tentacles, resembling a small sea anemone.

OPEN AND CLOSED POLYPS OF A CUP CORAL *(Tubastrea)*

There are hundreds of different varieties of polyps belonging to the two main groups of corals existing in the reef.

STONY CORALS

These polyps secrete calcareous material extracted from the water, creating a skeleton within the soft tissue of the polyp, into which it can retract for protection.

All stony coral polyps have six or a multiple of six tentacles. Most stony corals are built by numerous interconnecting colonies of polyps (hundreds of thousands) that, through the years, can build big formations. When these polyps die, they leave behind a calcareous skeleton, forming a base for other polyps and for the building of huge rock walls of the reef.

SOFT CORALS

Most polyps of this group do not build calcareous skeletons. With the exception of very few species, soft corals are not involved directly in the formation of coral reefs. These polyps have eight tentacles. The soft skeleton of these corals disappears when the polyps die and does not contribute to the mass of the coral reef.

CORAL REEF BUILDERS

These photographs show a few of the important reef-building stony corals. Even though most soft corals do not play a part in the building of reefs, in the Red Sea there is an exception in the pipe-organ coral (Tubipora musica). The fire coral is not classified as a true coral, but is one of the important members, especially in the shallow waters.

This area is priveleged to have some of the richest varieties of corals (both stony and soft) which together display a fantastic world of different polyps and create an incredible symphony of shapes and colours. Here the visitor can view the magic of the coral reefs and appreciate the colourful and complex equilibrium of this ecosystem.

Again, let us contribute to the effort to protect this fragile world for future generations.

POLYPS OF A SOFT CORAL *(SARCOPHYTON QLAUCUM)*

POLYPS IN FAN CORAL

POLYPS OF AN OCTO-CORAL

THE ONE OPEN POLYP OF THE MUSHROOM CORAL (FUNGIA)

13

DIVING THE CORAL REEFS

Scuba and snorkel diving are becoming increasingly popular. Millions of pople all over the world swim, snorkel, and scuba dive throughout the year, mainly in the tropical seas. A giant tourist industry for divers is widespread today in the different coral reef areas. The wonders of life in the seas attract nature lovers who, through their dive masks, can view this marvelous world. Through the years, some diving sites have become very famous; for example, the South Pacific, Australia, the Caribbean, Indian Ocean and the Red Sea have become the most attractive dive destinations. The Red Sea is known as a diver's paradise. The richness of this Sea and the easy access to the sites have contributed to the development over the last few years of numerous diving facilities on land and the arrival of dive vessels, bringing people to offshore reefs for snorkeling and scuba diving. There one finds a fantastic variety of choices in a diversity of islands and submerged reefs offering breathtaking underwater landscapes in shallow waters as well as on deep drop-offs.

Along the coast of the Sinai peninsula, from Eilat-Aqaba and southwards, fringing reefs close to the shore allow easy dives from various sites. Some of these are shallow reefs suitable for beginners and others are deep, vertical drop-offs for expert scuba divers only. All of them display the richness of the coral reefs with their incredible variety of fish and invertebrates, both common and rare specimens, that hypnotize thousands of enthusiastic admirers who return again and again finding a competely new experience in each dive.

14

SURVEYING CAVES AND CRACKS IN THE REEF

THE DIVER AND THE MAJESTIC EMPEROR FISH

Many of these areas have been declared national parks, thereby protecting and preserving the marine life for the benefit of today's and future generations. There are constant educational campaigns to preserve these reefs. The motto of the Ras Muhammed National Park is "take nothing with you, leave only bubbles behind".

GROUP OF DIVERS LOOKING FOR PHOTOGRAPHY TARGETS

15

THE DOLPHINS

Among marine mammals, the whales, dolphins, and dugongs (sea cow) found in this area, we will mention, in general, only the dolphins. This intelligent creature is now of great concern to humanity as an endangered species, mainly due to man's methods of fishing and interference in the natural balance of the animals' reproduction. Like humans, dolphins are warm-blooded, air-breathing mammals that evolved from a parallel, though unrelated, group of ancestors to those of humans.

This fascinating creature, the dolphin, with its highly-developed intelligence and ingenuity, has the acute capacity of communicating with humans through different ways of behavior and training techniques very popular today in different parts of the world.

DOLPHIN ENCOUNTER

SMILING TO THE OUTSIDE WORLD

In this short chapter, we feel that an important concern is the protection of the dolphin, whose survival is so closely related to the human species. Today, the media (communications, television, films, books, etc.) and also some marine parks, are making great efforts. to make the plight of these creatures known to humans, and heighten human understanding and awareness of the need to preserve these animals in nature for coming generations.

As a group, the dolphin is not as threatened as much as many other animals, however with the attention given to it by environmental groups around the world, it has become the focus animal used to help people understand the need to protect nature.

DOLPHIN LANDSCAPE

The continuous observation of these intelligent creatures in different parts of the world has enabled a better understanding of their behaviour and led to improved conditions for those still in captivity.

SWIMMING WITH DOLPHINS

DOLPHIN WATCHING A PORCUPINE PUFFER FISH

They are now generally kept in large and sufficiently deep facilities in the sea closed off with nets or in huge artificial pools, and attempts are made to provide their basic needs.

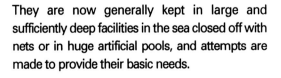

INTERACTION BETWEEN DIVERS

S H A R K S

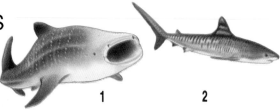

1   2   3   4

IMPRESSIVE CLOSE-UP OF AN OPEN WATER SHARK *(CARCHARINUS SP.)*

THE HAMMERHEAD SHARK *(SPHYRNA MOCARRAN)*
IN THE OPEN WATERS

S harks have always been fascinating to all peoples. Many stories and legends surrounding this fish have created a probably exaggerated reputation of this "dangerous to man" creature. There are approximately 350 species (varieties) of sharks in all of the oceans and some 35 of those are found in our area. Most of them are harmless to man and only a few species are potentially dangerous. Most sharks are fish predators, some also feeding on crabs, squid and sea birds. The big predators also feed on marine mammals (sea lions, dolphins etc.).

In the fish kingdom, sharks reach the largest sizes. In our area, we can find the representative of the biggest shark in all the seas — the "whale shark".

Whale shark:
When reaching adulthood, attains lengths of up to 18 meters (60 feet). Solitary in open waters, feeding on plantonic organisms (small marine creatures floating in the open water), this huge creature is harmless to man, and only his great dimensions are the reason for the great respect shown to this shark.

Tiger shark:
When adult also attains large dimensions (up to 6 m (20 ft)). Swims solitarily in open waters and is considered potentially dangerous to man. His name is derived from the stripes and markings similar to tiger skin.

Mako shark:
Another very impressive shark characterized by its speed and potentially dangerous to man. Has very sharp and long teeth and is found in open waters solitarily swimming offshore. Attains lengths of up to 5 m (15 ft.).

5

6

4

Oceanic white tip shark:
Another impressive shark suspected to be responsible for attacks on man in open waters. Swims close to the surface in deep water areas and sometimes seen by divers in the southern part of the Gulf close to the reef wall formations. Attains 4 m (13 ft).

5

Hammerhead shark:
His unusual head shape is the reason for his popular name. Can be seen often in big schools in the open waters. Occasionally individuals may be seen close to shore and coral reefs. One of the biggest predatory sharks — can reach 8 m (40 ft) in length.

6

Sand bar shark:
This deep water shark, with its remarkably high and impressive dorsal fin, is found close to the bottom of the sea at depths of 150 to 350 m. Common in our area and attains 3 m (10 ft).

7

Grey reef shark:
In many instances, divers in the southern area of the Gulf have reported seeing this shark, often in shallow water, solitary or in groups (during mating season). Attains 2 m (7 ft).

8

Black tip reef shark:
Very common in the shallows of the coral reefs, individually or in small groups. Typical black-tipped dorsal fin can be seen from shore sticking out from the surface of the water. Attains up to 1.80 m (6 ft).

9

White tip reef shark:
Another quite common shark found often by scuba divers during the day lying in the openings of caves at different depths and very active swimmer at night. Attains 1.50 m (5 ft).

1-2-3

Leopard shark (1A) — guitar shark (2A) — angel shark (3A):
These fish are representative of a group of harmless bottom sharks found on sandy bottoms at different depths. Feed on small creatures living in the area. Attain up to 2.50 m (8 ft) length.

A SILVER-TIP SHARK IN A DRAMATIC LANDSCAPE *(CARCHARINUS ALBIMARGINATUS)*

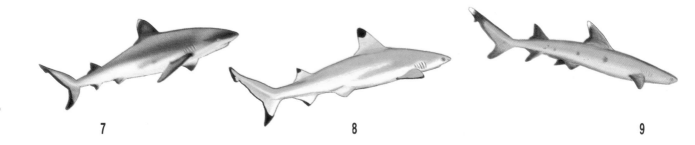

7

8

9

A SILVER TIP SHARK *(CARCHARINUS ALBIMARGINATUS)* IN OPEN WATERS

CLOSE-UP OF A SILVER TIP SHARK

A WHITE TIP REEF SHARK *(TRIANDDON OBESUS)* SWIMMING IN THE REEF AREA

1 A

2 A

3 A

25

COMMENSALS

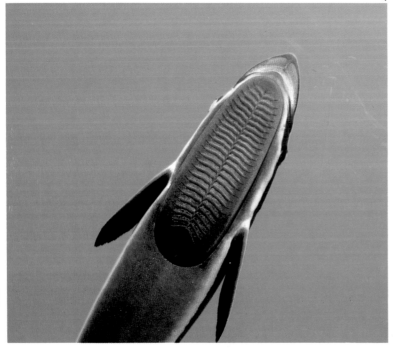

A very interesting symbiotic phenomenon is the pilot fish and sucker fish often accompanying large sharks where the number of commensals following the shark is relative to the size of the shark. The pilots swim on the sides of and ahead of the shark and appear to be guiding the big fish. The suckers attach themselves to different areas of the shark's skin by a vacuum-type mechanism on top of their bodies. Big sharks can be followed by dozens of commensals which mainly share the leftover food of the host and also clean parasites from the shark's skin. The commensals, in turn, feel protected by the shark from potential enemies in the water.

THE SUCKER FISH ATTACHED MECHANISM

EAGLE RAYS — STING RAYS — ELECTRIC RAYS

THE EAGLE RAY *(AETOBATUS NARINARI)* SWIMMING IN OPEN WATERS RESEMBLING A BIG BIRD

1

2

Rays belong to a group of fish closely related to the shark (cartilaginous). The huge manta rays, reaching up to 6 m (20 ft) to eagle rays *(1)* are continuously swimming in the open waters. They look like beautiful big birds flying in the water, displaying an amazing spectacle when as individuals, pairs or groups they are occasionally watched by divers.

The rest of the group of rays (sting rays) *(2)* swim less and most of the time they remain buried in the sandy sea bottom where they also find food consisting of clams, shrimps and other creatures living in the sand. Only the manta rays are plankton (small, microscopic life in the open water) feeders. Eagle rays and sting rays have venomous spines in different areas of their tail. These spines secrete a strong venom (poison) when stinging which can be very painful and can have serious consequences for man.

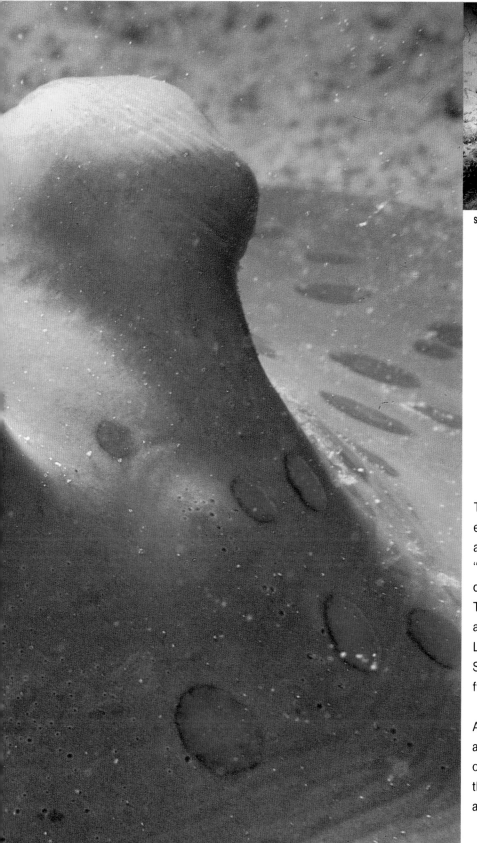

BLUE SPOTTED STING RAY HEAD

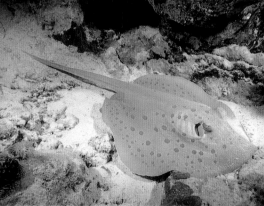

SPOTTED STING RAY *(DASCYATIS LYMMA)* **IN HIS NATURAL HABITAT (3)**

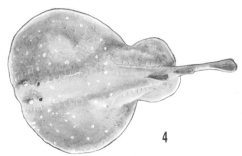

4

The torpedo electric ray **(4)** is an interesting and unique marine fish that has a large muscular organ which becomes "battery-like", giving out a powerful electric shock when handled or stepped on. This electric shock is used as protection against an enemy or to paralyze its prey. Lives mostly buried in sandy bottoms. Small in size — attains up to 30 cm (1 ft) in length.

All of the various ray groups are quiet and friendly towards humans and the ones having venomous spines will use them only as protection against an enemy.

HEAD OF A GREAT BARRACUDA *(SPHYRAENA BARRACUDA)*

1

Together with sharks, barracudas are famous for their reputation as dangerous to man. Again, exaggerated stories and legends give this fish its bad name, while there is very little proof of attacks on humans. This elongated, cylindrical bodied fish can reach 3 m long *(1)* (The Great Barracuda) can be seen most of the time solitary in open waters. Occasionally found in schools searching for food. These are carnivorous, feeding mainly on living fish, squid, etc.

Another species — the Melita, small-sized barracuda, reaching up to 50 cm (1.5 ft) and is always found in numerous schools in open waters close to coral formations.

SCHOOL OF MIDDLE-SIZED BARRACUDAS *(SPHYRAENA JELLO)* **IN OPEN WATERS**

THE CORAL FISHES

A fascinating and interesting fish population is characteristic of the tropical coral reefs in different seas. The Red Sea and, in particular, the Gulf of Aqaba, contains an incredible variety and concentration of different species, among them some families of extremely colorful and unique beauty which bring well-deserved admiration.

SHINING IN ITS BEAUTIFUL BLUE AND YELLOW COLORS — THE MACULOSUS ANGEL (POMACANTHUS MACULOSUS)

1A   1B

ANGEL FISHES

THE MACULOSUS ANGEL — A CLOSE-UP OF THE HEAD

The so-called Angel Fishes are typical inhabitants of the coral formations and are frequently found close to cave openings, solitarily or, during the mating season, in pairs. Only the Jenicant Angel *(1A-1B)* lives in schools in the deep open waters.

The Queen Angel *(1)*, one of the most beautiful representatives of the family, is found in all of the Indo-Pacific tropical reefs. Amazing color combinations attract attention especially to this species among all the others.

1

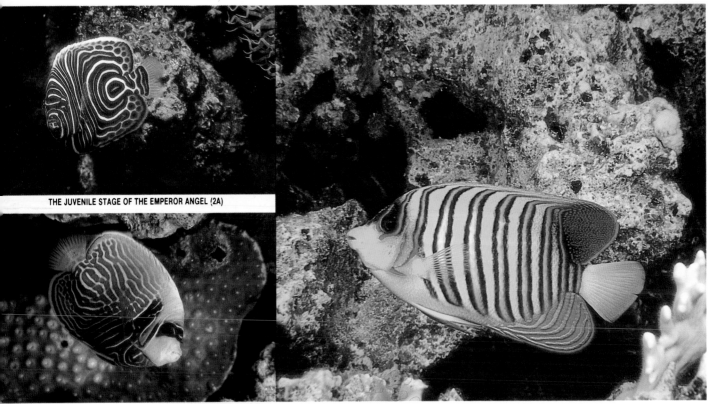

THE JUVENILE STAGE OF THE EMPEROR ANGEL (2A)

THE INTERMEDIARY STAGE OF EMPEROR ANGEL (2B)

THE MAGNIFICENT FINAL STAGE OF THE EMPEROR ANGEL
(POMACANTHUS IMPERATOR) (2C)

Another beautiful representative of this family is the Emperor Angel *(2)* which has an interesting phenomenon occurring in different stages of its life. The white color rings on its body characterize its juvenile stage in life *(2A)*. In the intermediary stage, we can see the first yellow lines *(2B)* which afterwards are dominant during the adult period *(2C)*. For many years, these three apparently different fish were classified by science with different names. Aquarium observations allowed the discovery that the three are actually the same fish.

The same phenomenon occurs in the Asfur Angel *(3)* and the Maculosus Angel *(4)*. The Asfur Angel, with its beautiful yellow and blue, is a species found only in the Red Sea (Endemic).

The Yellow-Ear Angel *(5)* and the Multispine Angel (6) are also found only in the Red Sea (Endemic).

5

6

3

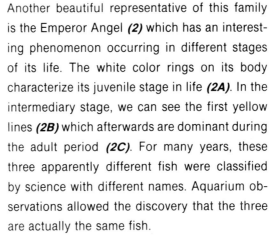

4

THE BUTTERFLY FISHES

THE UNIQUE "ONLY IN THE RED SEA" MASKED BUTTERFLY
(CHAETODON SEMILARVATUS) PAIRING IN THE REEF

Another impressive and beautiful family typical of the fish population in the coral reefs. The compressed shape and the capricious colors combine to immediately attract attention and admiration of this strange creature that Mother Nature created.

Of the 14 varieties of Butterfly Fishes in the Red Sea, seven are indigenous to this area only. These are found in pairs or small groups feeding on small creatures from the reef.

The following species described in this book are found "only in the Red Sea": the Masked Butterfly *(1)*, the Red Tail Butterfly *(2)*, the Austrian Butterfly *(3)*, the Orange Face Butterfly *(4)*, The Brown Striped Butterfly *(5)*, the Arrow Striped Butterfly *(9)* and the Horn Antenna Butterfly *(11)*. The others are distributed throughout the Indo-Pacific coral reefs *(6-7-8-10-12)*.

The largest specimens of *(1)* and *(6)* reach up to 30 cm (1 ft).
The deep water Butterfly *(12)* is found only in very deep waters below 150 meters.

1

2

3

4

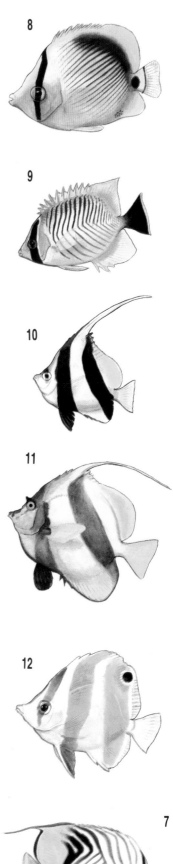

A SCHOOL OF HORN ANTENNA BUTTERFLY FISH IN THEIR
NATURAL HABITAT- *(HENIOCHUS INTERMEDIUS)*

THE BROWN STRIPED BUTTERFLY *(CHAETODON FASCIATUS)* —
ANOTHER "UNIQUE IN THE RED SEA" — SWIMMING IN THE CRYSTAL
WATERS OF THIS REEF

THE SOHAL SURGEON (ACANTHURUS SOHAL) SWIMMING IN SHALLOWS OF THE REEF

A SCHOOL OF SOHAL'S SURGEONS IN THE SHALLOW REEF TABLE

This family is represented in the reef area by some very attractive and interesting behavior of the species. This popular name comes from the distinguished possession of one or more spines or lateral scalpel-like protruberance close to the tail, which by a side sweep of the tail can inflict a very painful sting or cut in other fish or in humans who do not know how to handle this fish. This is a defense mechanism against enemies.

Most of the surgeon fishes are vegetarian feeders. Some of them are remarkably colorful and a few species are indigenous (endemic) only to the Red Sea, such as the Sohal Surgeon *(1)* and the Blue Tang *(3)*, both distinguished for their beautiful color combination. Others, such as the Orange-spine Surgeon *(2)* or the Sailfin Surgeon *(4)* are spread throughout all of the Indo-Pacific tropical coral reefs.

A UNICORN SURGEON FISH IN OPEN WATERS

4

1

2

40

TRIGGER-FILE FISHES

Most of the Trigger Fishes are typical inhabitants of the coral reefs. In our area we have a diverse variety, some of them also indigenous (endemic) to the Red Sea.

The name is derived from a (trigger-like) spine in the first dorsal fin which can be locked with another small spine near the first. This mechanism permits the fish to enter crevices in the reef and lock the trigger in the coral wall, thereby making it impossible for its predators to pull it out.

THE HARLEQUIN FILE FISH (OXYMONOCANTHUS HALLI)
IS A DELICATE, SMALL (5 CM) FISH BETWEEN THE CORALS

41

42

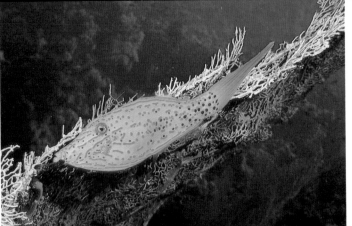

THE SCRAWLED FILE FISH *(OSBECKIA SCRIPTA)*
INDIVIDUAL-CLOSE TO A SEA-FAN (7)

A very attractive representative of this family and also found only in the Red Sea is the so-called "Picasso Fish" *(1)* whose capricious color design is reminiscent of the conceptions of the famous painter.

Most of the species, such as the Orange Striped Trigger Fish *(2)*, the Blue Throat Trigger Fish (indigenous) *(3)* and the Titan Trigger Fish *(5)* live individually or in pairs, also the Blue Fuscos Trigger Juvenile *(6a)* and Adult *(6)* while the Red Tooth Trigger Fish *(4)* is found in schools close to the coral formations.

THE FILE TRIGGER — AN UNUSUAL FISH *(MONOCANTHUS SP.)*

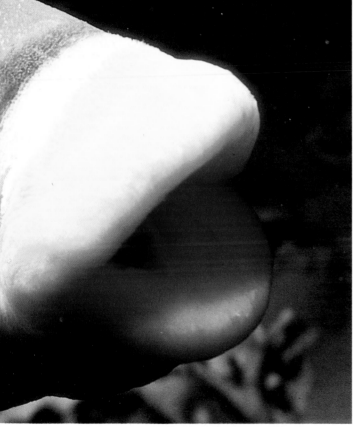

The File Fishes, closely related to the Trigger Fishes, have a thin spine in the dorsal fin which can also be locked. There are several species in the area. One of the most attractive and interesting shapes is the Scrawled File Fish *(7)* found all over the tropical seas, reaching lengths of up to 65 cm (2 ft).

PARROT **F**ISHES

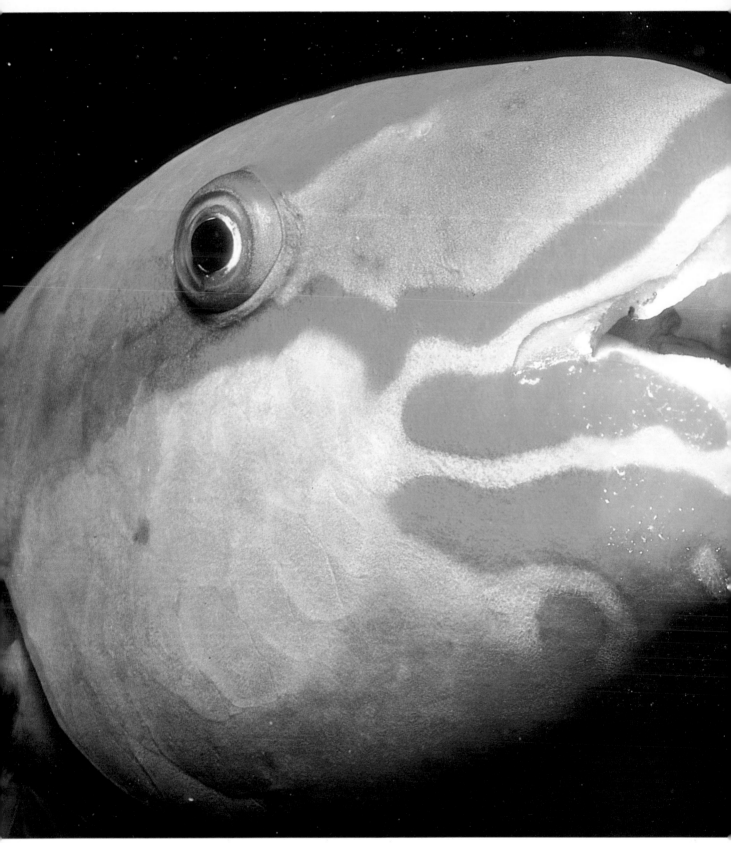

CLOSE-UP OF THE HEAD OF A PARROT-FISH WELL-NAMED FOR ITS COLORS AND MOUTH *(SCARUS SP)*

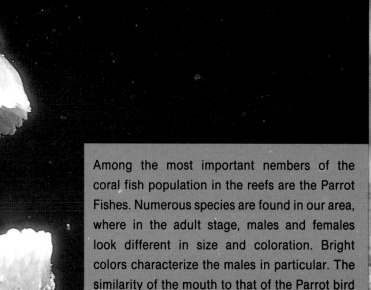

Among the most important nembers of the coral fish population in the reefs are the Parrot Fishes. Numerous species are found in our area, where in the adult stage, males and females look different in size and coloration. Bright colors characterize the males in particular. The similarity of the mouth to that of the Parrot bird is the reason for this name.

These fish are herbivores and feed on algae scraped from the limestone coral rock with their strong teeth. The rock is ground into sand with the algae and the algae is digested by the fish. Like other vegetarian fish, parrot fishes feed during the day and divers can distinctly hear the scraping noise of feeding between the corals. During the night, the parrot fish sleep close to coral ledges or small caves and they secrete a transparent mucus around their whole body which possibly protects them from enemies. Adults of some species can reach sizes of up to around 60 cm (2 ft).

We present in this book only some representatives of the many species which are found in the area and can be seen swimming in the reefs, individually or in schools.

A SCHOOL OF WHITE PARROT FISH FEEDING ON THE REEF (SCARUS SP.)

A COLORFUL MALE PARROT FISH *(SCARUS SP.)* IN A COLORFUL REEF BACKGROUND

A COLORFUL MALE PARROT FISH *(SCARUS SP.)* IN THE REEF

A PARROT FISH *(SCARUS SP.)* RESTING CLOSE TO A CORAL FORMATION AT NIGHT

46

OPEN WATERS NEAR THE REEF

Within the whole population of the reef area, we cannot ignore the large variety of individuals or schools of fish present in the open water — from the surface to all depths — giving an important landscape appearance to the blue waters of the open sea.

TWINSPOT SNAPPER *(LUTIANUS)* **SCHOOLING IN A REEF VICINITY**

In the surface area, we can see elongated silver needle fishes *(1)-(2)* searching and hunting little living fish which are the favorite prey of this very fast swimming fish.

One of the most important inhabitants of open water shallows are the big schools of the fish popularly known as the "Blue Fish" *(3)*, a relatively small fish, reaching 30 cm in size. These schools provide a spectacular sight to divers when passing by in the hundreds with their bright bluish body color, with yellow lines in some species.

The Bat Fish *(4)* with its flat round body and delicate appearance is found in big schools of adults (reaching 40 cm) close to the drop-offs and always in compact formations.

48

1

2

3

4

A GIANT FISH SOLITARY IN THE REEF

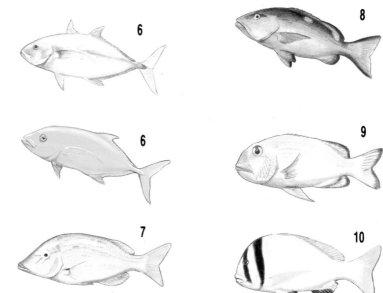

There still remains a vast variety of other families and species of fish found in open waters in reef areas.

5A

With their predominantly silver background color, the different varieties of jack fishes *(5)* *(5A)* (juvenile) *(6)*, some reaching 90 cm long, swimming in schools and sometimes individually or in small groups, make a strong impact on the fish population.

The various species of snappers or emperors *(7)* blue spots, the *(8)* red, the *(9)* big eye and the *(10)* double bar bream are only a few of the huge varieties also swimming close to the reefs in small or large schools. Adults reach 45-60 cm.

These are only some of the different species of the open water fish population, so important in the entire dense marine life in or close to the reefs.

WRASSES

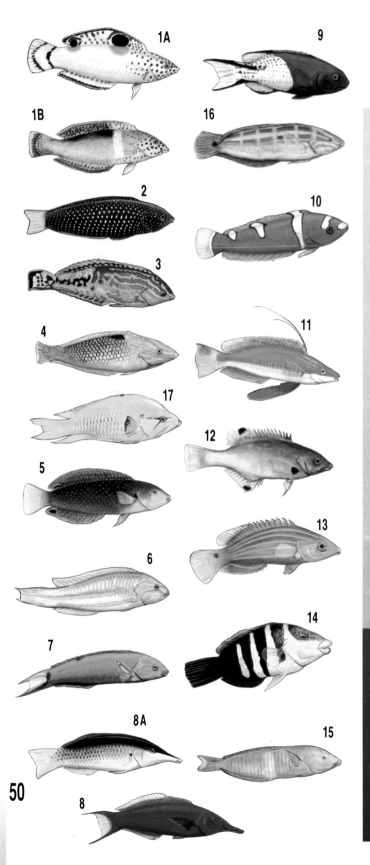

In all of the Indo-Pacific coral reefs, the Wrasse family have the highest diversity of species, especially in the Red Sea where more than 60 varieties are found, from very tiny size to the huge Humphead Wrasse (reaching up to 2 m long (7 ft) and 800 kg (1600 pounds) in weight).

Most of the wrasses are brightly colored. Juveniles frequently have different colors to adults, changing during the different stages in their life *(1A-B-C)*. Many males have different colors from females (also for many years some of them were considered to be separate species). Scientists discovered during recent years that many wrasses (as in other families of fish) develop a very interesting phenomenon called "sex reversal". It was found that in many species, they start the adult stage of life as females and later they may alter their sex to male, including changing colors. This process may happen when for different reasons it becomes necessary to balance the population of males or females.

DIVER CLOSE TO A HUGE HUMPHEAD WRASSE *(CHEILINUS UNDULATUS)* IN THE REEF WALL

▲ **BANDCHEEK WRASSE** *(CHEILINUS DIAGRAMMUS)* **ENJOYING THE CLEANER WRASSE** *(LABROIDES DIMIDIATUS)*

▲
▲ *(CHEILINUS MENTALIS)* **SMALL DELICATE WRASSE BETWEEN CORAL POLYPS**

▲
▲
▲ **SQUARE DESIGN BODY COLORS IN THIS NICE WRASSE** *(HALICHOERES CENTRIQUADRUS)*

THE LINED WRASSE *(ANAMPSES LINEATUS)* **BETWEEN ALGAE AND SEA GRASS**

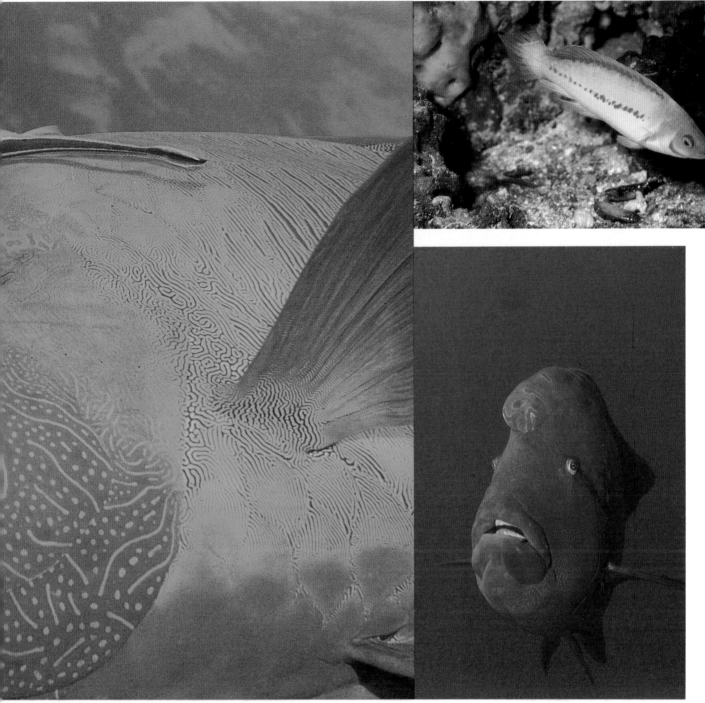

HUMPHEAD OR NAPOLEON WRASSE WITH A REMORA SUCKER FISH   MAJESTIC-LOOKING HUMPHEAD WRASSE

Wrasses are carnivorous, feeding mostly on small creatures which they look for during the day in various areas of the coral reef. Some also swim in the open water close to the reef formation.

In this chapter on wrasses, we present only some of the most remarkable and representative of the family, many of them very familiar to divers.

A WRASSE *(CHEILINUS SP.)* **RESTING ON A SOFT CORAL** *(LITOPHYTON SP.)*

AN ADULT NAPOLEON WRASSE *(CORIS AYGULA)* **SWIMMING ON THE REEF**

54

THE BANDED CLEANER SHRIMP *(STENOPUS HISPIDUS)* **ON A SPONGE**

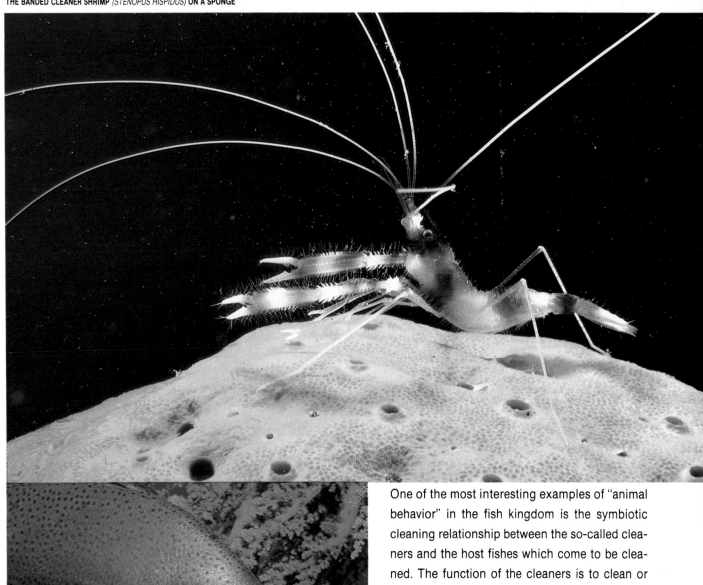

One of the most interesting examples of "animal behavior" in the fish kingdom is the symbiotic cleaning relationship between the so-called cleaners and the host fishes which come to be cleaned. The function of the cleaners is to clean or eat the parasites attached to the skin, gills or even the inside of the mouth opening of the host.

Generally, the cleaners are small creatures, fish or shrimps, which quite often approach very large fish. The host fish knows the function of the cleaners and the necessity of their getting rid of the parasites which in turn become food for the cleaners.

In field observations in nature, the cleaners stay in what is called "cleaning stations" in the reef. In this case, the cleaner wrasse *(1)*, found in pairs, can be observed cleaning different kinds of fish, most of them approaching the station from the vicinity, and sometimes waiting patiently in turn to be cleaned by the cleaners.

55

BIG FISH ARE OFTEN CLEANED BY THE TINY CLEANER WRASSE

It is amazing .to see large fish being cleaned by these small ones, sometimes entering the gill opening or the interior of the mouth without endangering the cleaner. In field observations, the author was witness to big sharks approaching the reef and being cleaned by cleaner wrasses.

Not only the typical cleaner wrasse has this function, however, and it is very common to see other wrasses, butterfly fish, angel fish and others, during the juvenile stage of life, also cleaning various other fish. Different varieties of shrimps, especially the Banded Coral Cleaner Shrimp (Page 43) are common cleaners.

THE CLEANER WRASSE *(LABROIDES DIMIDIATUS)*
WAITING FOR THE NEXT FISH TO BE CLEANED

A COMMON LION FISH *(PTEROIS VOLITANS)* — MAGNIFICENT, UNUSUAL SHAPE OF FISH

In the family of the Scorpion Fishes in our area, two unique and strangely shaped representatives of interesting behavior are the Lion Fishes. The Common Lion Fish *(1)* and the Red Lion Fish *(2)* are both amongst the most impressive and eye-catching fish. The Lion Fish *(1)* is very common in our reefs, actively looking for prey (small fish, crabs) during the sunrise or sunset hours, or in dark, shaded areas during the day. Swimming slowly with all of its elongated dorsal and pectoral fins spread makes this incredible creature one of the most typically amazing fish in the coral reef.

The Red Lion Fish *(2)*, less common than the other, is active hunting for prey during the night hours and is also very impressive with the contrasting white and red colors on its body.

As in all the members of the Scorpion Fishes family, the Lion Fishes are highly venomous. The venom found in the spines of the dorsal and anal fins can inflict very painful stings on humans which can also result in serious health complications (Page 114). No doubt that the poisonous spines are used by these fish for protective defense against their enemies in the sea as well as against man when he tries to touch or disturb them.

THE RED LION FISH *(PTERIOS RADIATA)* **AT NIGHT IN THE REEF VICINITY**

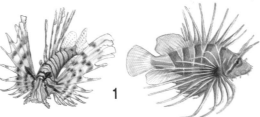

1
2

58

The popular name of Scorpion Fish comes from the venomous spines possessed by most of the varieties of this family.

SCORPION FISHES

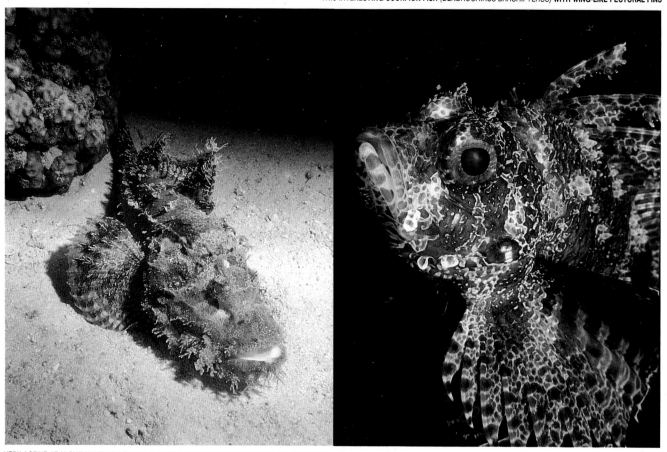

VERY ACTIVE AT NIGHT HUNTING FOR PREY, THIS SCORPION FISH *(SCORPENOPSUS CIRRHOSA)* , IS ALSO WELL CAMOUFLAGED (1)

The Scorpion Fish lives on the bottom of the sea close to or between rocks or corals with a fantastic mimetic appearance which makes it very difficult to notice their location clearly. These are predators of small fish which also do not notice the presence of the Scorpion Fish. Nearly 30 different varieties are found in the Red Sea, however we are only mentioning the most common ones in our area.

The venomous mechanism, as in all of the family, is located in the dorsal and anal fins. It is also a protective defense and becomes very dangerous to humans when stung. In the various species, the poison has different potencies. A sting from these fish is extremely painful and serious complications can result without the correct treatment (Page 115).

59

STONE FISHES

Stone Fishes, also belonging to the Scorpion Fish family, are the most perfect in camouflage on the sea floor between rocks or corals. They resemble a rock or stone, therefore the derivation of their name.

The famous Stone Fish *(1)* and the Telescopic Stone Fish *(2)* are the two classic representatives in our waters.

The venomous mechanism is similar to that of the Scorpion Fish, but the potency of the poison is extremely dangerous to man. Wounds from the venomous spines can cause serious complications and, in some cases, unbelieveable agony and death.

For all Scorpion Fish family wounds, the first emergency treatment is to IMMERSE the injured area in water as HOT as can be tolerated and elevate the area. Medical attention should be sought as soon as possible in extreme cases.

RESEMBLING A ROCK, THE STONE FISH CAN STAY FOR HOURS IN THE SAME LOCATION (1)

2

TWO SNOWFLAKE MORAY EELS
(ECHIDNA NEBULOSA) —
A RARE CLOSE-UP DIFFICULT TO FIND

Reminding most people of a "snake", moray eels are unmistakeably fishes with the characteristic elongated, muscular body. They live in hiding during the day in crevices, small caves in the coral reef, while during the night they are more active looking for prey.

SIMILAR TO A SNAKE — THIS EEL *(MYRICHTYS MACULOSUS)* **IS FOUND IN SANDY BOTTOMS**

THE HEAD OF A GREY MORAY *(ECHIDNA GRISEA)* **STICKING OUT OF A CORAL ROCK HOLE COVERED BY A RED SPONGE**

Some species can reach very great lengths, such as the Giant Moray which can attain 2.5 — 3 m (10 ft) and 20 cm in diameter. Most have sharp canine teeth and they can inflict a strong bite *(1)*, but only when provoked, meaning that they are not dangerous if they are not disturbed. They are not considered poisonous. In our area, the most common are the Grey Moray *(4)*, the Snowflake Moray *(3)* and the Yellow-mouth Moray *(2)*.

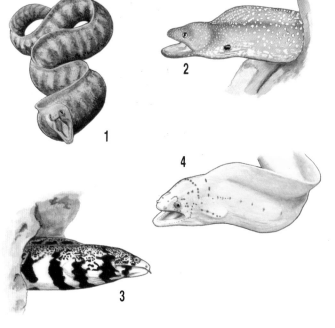

GARDEN EELS

Every diver who searches in some sandy and grass-bottomed sloped areas can see a beautiful and incredible spectacle of many hundreds or thousands of these elongated creatures sticking out of the sand. They are called Garden Eels. Close relatives to the Moray Eels, Garden Eels live in big colonies in holes dug by them in the sand. When they are searching for food (small organisms in the open water brought by currents), three-quarters of their elongated bodies can be seen erected out of the sand. When in danger, they can retreat into the holes very fast, disappearing immediately.

Divers can easily see how this shy creature gets inside the hole when approaching it closely.

AN INDIVIDUAL GARDEN EEL
WATCHING TWO DIVERS
APPROACHING

THE SHY GARDEN EEL LOOKING
ALL AROUND BEFORE EMERGING
FROM THE SAND (1)

64

A F T E R   S U N S E T — B E F O R E   S U N R I S E
S Q U I R R E L *F* I S H E S — *B* IG *E* YES

A SQUIRREL FISH OR SOLDIER FISH *(MYRIPRISTIS MURDJAN)* COMING OUT OF A CAVE

This group of fishes has a nocturnal behavior (active at night). They live during the day mostly in caves or in openings of big crevices or shelves in the reef.

At sunset, they leave the diurnal shelters and swim the whole night to open waters searching for food. They are predators of small fish or crustaceans and they have excellent sight in the dark. At sunrise, they return to their diurnal shelters.

Squirrel fish are found in groups or in large schools.

THE BIG EYE *(PRIACANTHUS HAMRUR)* AT NIGHT SEARCHING FOR FOOD

1   2   3

65

THE **G**OLDFISH

Of the thousands of fish populating the Red Sea coral reefs, the Goldfish is the most abundant. Huge schools of thousands give a dominant background among all the other coral fishes. The red color of the Goldfish also gives a predominant reddish landscape to the whole reef coloration.

The males *(1)* and the females *(2)* look different and of the numerous fish in each school there exists a proportional number of females (approximately 10) for each male. In this family of fish, there also exists the interesting phenomenon of "sex reversal", the disappearing of a male from the groups, resulting in one of the females assuming the male role, also changing the colors of the body.

The Goldfish is a typical schooling fish, during the day keeping a short distance from the coral head where it finds shelter when in danger and at night, a place to hide.

66

A SCHOOL OF FEMALE GOLDFISH BETWEEN SOFT CORALS

A MAGNIFICENT MALE DEEP WATER GOLDFISH *(ANTHIAS TEANIATUS)*   PART OF A SCHOOL OF COMMON GOLDFISH *(ANTHIAS SQUAMIPINNIS)* IN THE REEF

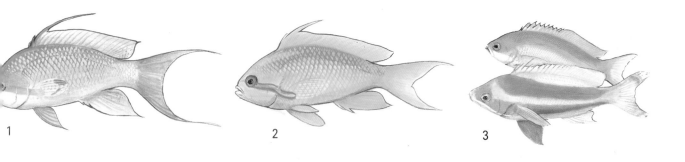

1   2   3

SWEEPERS

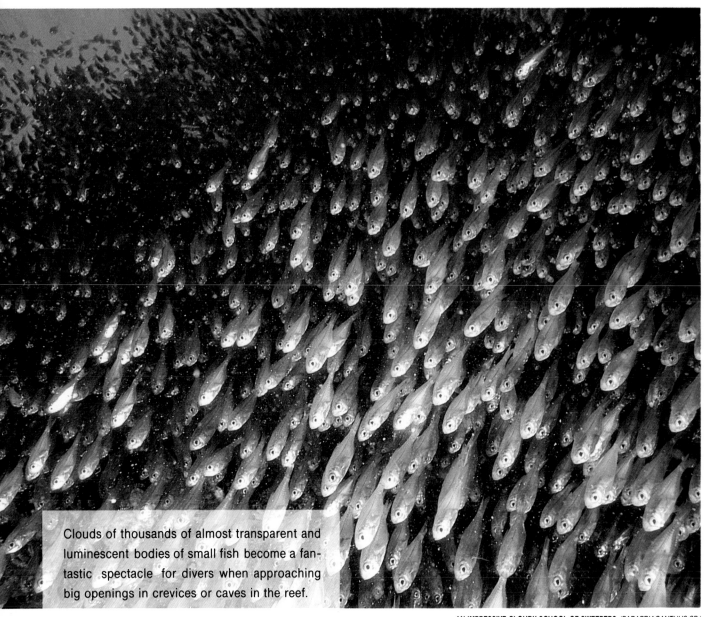

Clouds of thousands of almost transparent and luminescent bodies of small fish become a fantastic spectacle for divers when approaching big openings in crevices or caves in the reef.

AN IMPRESSIVE CLOUDY SCHOOL OF SWEEPERS *(PARAPRIACANTHUS SP.)* IN THE OPENING OF A BIG CAVE IN THE REEF (1)

The Transparent Sweeper *(1)* becomes a unique attraction for any diver, especially when swimming in between the schools of these aggregations.

The Triangular Sweeper *(2)* with its brilliant reddish reflection through the light and rapid movements is the other variety of this interesting fish.

68 Like Squirrel Fishes, Sweepers school in caves during the day and in open waters at night, searching for food.

CORAL FISHES — DAMSEL FISHES

THE YELLOW CORAL FISH *(DASCYLLUS MARGINATUS)* IN BETWEEN THE CORAL BRANCHES FOR PROTECTION

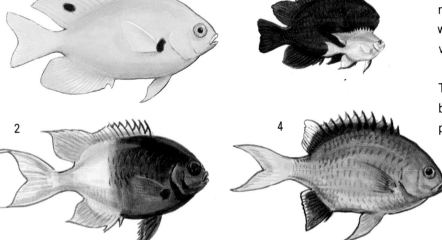

Coral and Damsel Fish are a large family of small and colorful fishes found in many varieties mostly in colonies or schools. Frequently shallow water inhabitants , they are territorial, and swim very close to coral formations.

The compressed body allows them to get in-between the coral branches or narrow crevices, protecting them from predators.

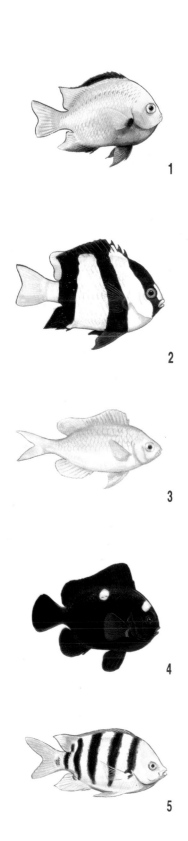

1

2

3

4

5

The Yellow *(1)*, and the Banded Coral Fish *(2)*, and the Green Chromis *(3)* can be commonly seen in the shallows in colonies close to branched stony corals. The Domino Coral Fish *(4)* displays different behavior when juvenile (3

cm); can be found close to and among sea anemones together with the Clown Fish (page 73)
and also occasionally among branched corals,
but when adult (12 cm) moves to big coral heads.
The Sergeant Major Damsel Fish *(5)*, one of

the biggest in the family (15 cm) is a very
common and well-known inhabitant of the fish
reef population found in colonies close to the
coral heads. Can be found in all tropical seas.

FLASHLIGHT **F**ISHES

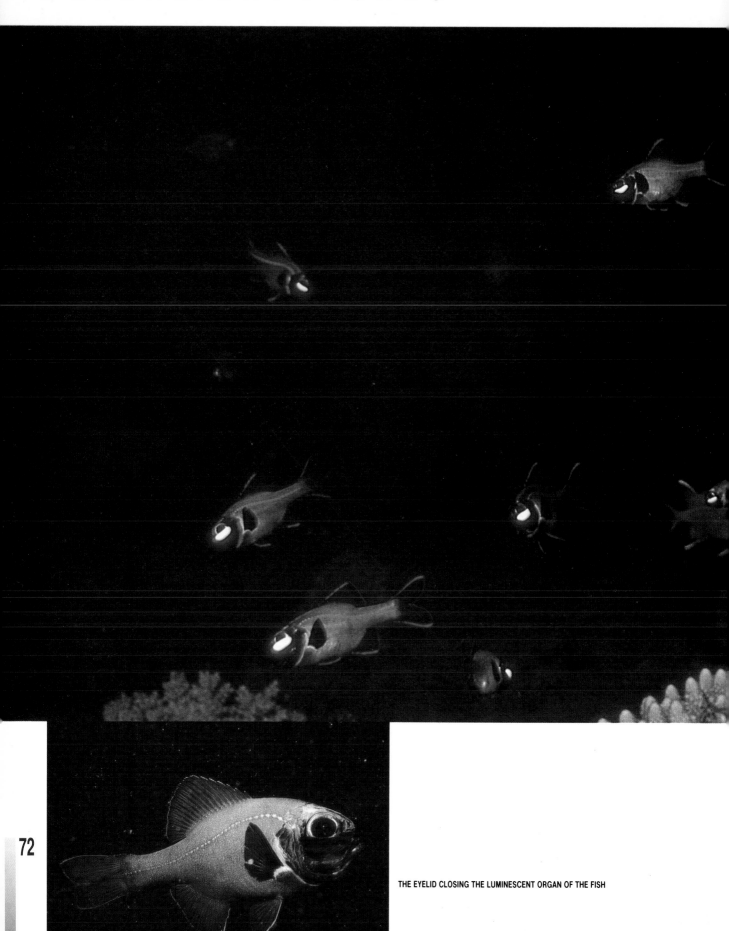

72

THE EYELID CLOSING THE LUMINESCENT ORGAN OF THE FISH

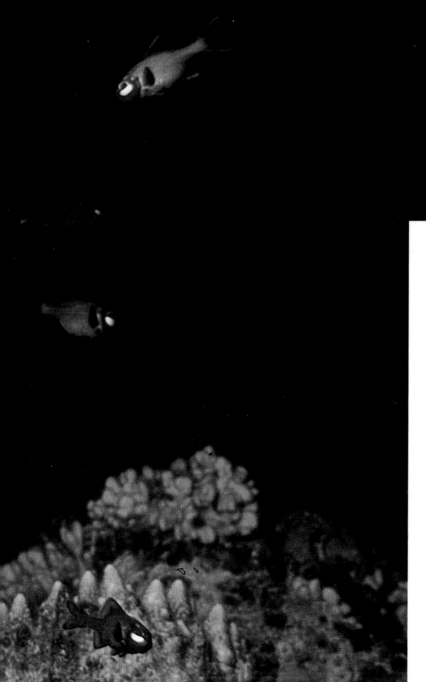

AN INDIVIDUAL FLASHLIGHT FISH — CLOSE-UP OF THE LUMINESCENT ORGAN UNDER THE EYE (2)

This is the Flashlight Fish. During the day these fish live in deep caves within the reef shallows in total darkness. On moonless nights they emerge into open waters in search of food. The luminescent organ below the eye is populated by numerous luminescent microscopic bacteria which probably feed on the fish blood system. There is an eyelid (hinged from below) which turns the light on and off. The light is used for attracting small organisms in the open water that constitute its food. The flickering of the light is also utilized as a warning or mating signal.

The Pine Cone Fish **(2)** also has a small luminescent organ close to the mouth that is also used to attract small life for food. Lives solitarily in the reef caves during the day and at night emerges to the open water in search of food.

In some areas, one of the most breathtaking spectacles to see from the shore at night is a big patch of light moving close to the surface of the water. If you then enter the water, with a mask, hundreds of luminescent spots can be seen moving and blinking.

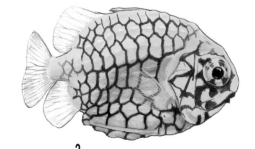

2

*G*ROUPERS

CLOSE-UP OF AN OPEN MOUTH OF THE RED CORAL GROUPER *(CEPHALOPOLIS MINIATA)*

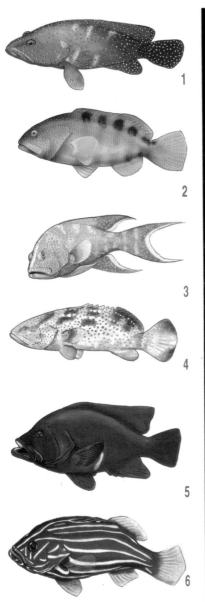

Popular and well-known family of fish, some of them very colorful and considered commercial fish, wanted very much by fishermen for their good taste.

Several species are found in our area, some of them reaching huge sizes. Occasionally divers have reported seeing Giant Groupers (around 2 m (7 ft)) and some fishermen have also reported catching this size Grouper *(4)*.

Other species such as *(1)*, *(2)*, *(3)*, *(5)* can reach 50-80 cm (2-2.5 ft).

74

A RED CORAL GROUPER BETWEEN A SCHOOL OF GOLDFISH SEARCHING FOR PREY

Groupers live in the coral reef close to or in caves or crevices and are predators of other fishes.

The Zebra Soap Fish *(6)*, a close relative of the Grouper, is a small (reaching 15 cm) and attractive fish which has the peculiarity of a soft mucus in the skin that possibly is toxic to other fish which are potential enemies.

*L*ITTLE *B*EAUTIES

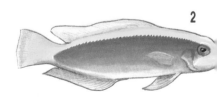

THE FRIDMAN FISH *(PSEUDOCHROMIS FRIDMANI)* —
CLOSE-UP OF THIS UNUSUALLY COLORED LITTLE BEAUTY

1

2

THE LEMON GOBY *(GOBIODON CITRINUS)*
ON THE BRANCHES OF A TABLE CORAL

In the family of the Dottybacks, two of them have amazing and unusual colors like the Fridman Fish *(1)*, discovered and named after David Fridman, one of the authors of this book. The fluorescent purple color of these small fish [4-5 cm (2 inches)] immediately attracts attention and its presence in the reefs becomes prominent. It lives on shady walls of the reefs and is quite common. The Sunrise Fish *(2)*, also small (4-5 cm, 2 inches), is relatively uncommon, but its prominent colors are also the subject of admiration of those who see it on sandy bottoms between small rocks or corals.

Among the branches of the big table corals, the Lemon Goby *(4)*, small lemon colored fish with graceful movements, attracts the attention of visitors to the surroundings, but is very well protected by the coral branches.

Amongst the different families of little coral fishes are some varieties with remarkably unusual colors, shapes and behavior.

We select in this chapter only a few of them from perhaps hundreds of others that can be included in this category of "Little Beauties".

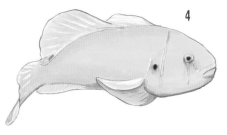

4

77

In deeper waters (below 30 m (100 ft)), between the branches of the sea fan corals, divers can see another small beautiful fish, the Longnose Hawkfish *(3)* with its delicate red and silver colors.

3

THE LONGNOSE HAWKFISH *(OXYCIRRHITES TYPUS)* ON A SOFT CORAL IN DEEP WATER

The Tricolor *(5)* can be seen close to coral formations in open water, searching for food, but when in danger quickly enters permanent holes which are shelter for protection day and night.

78

5

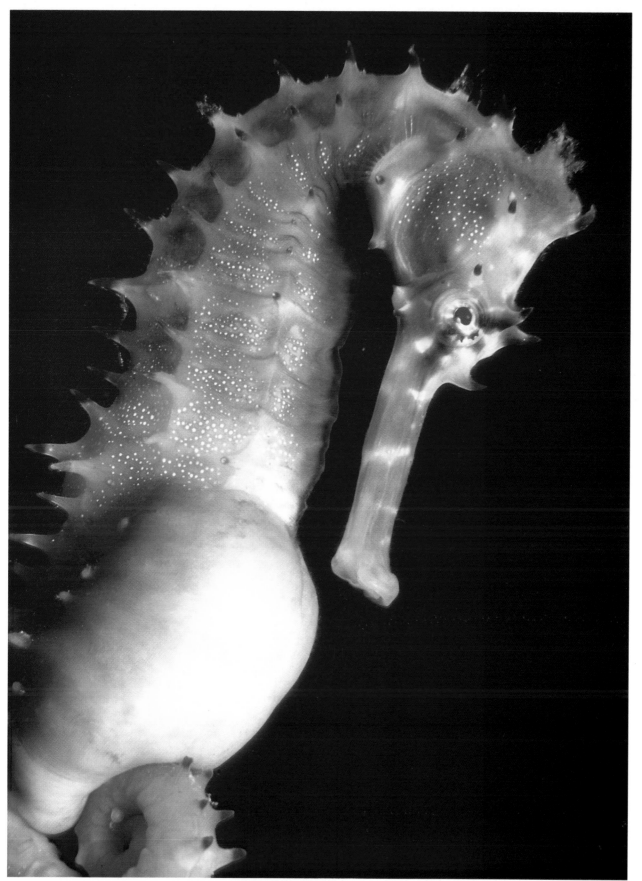

A PREGNANT MALE SEA HORSE *(HIPPOCAMPUS HISTRIX)* — **UNUSUAL REPRODUCTION BEHAVIOR**

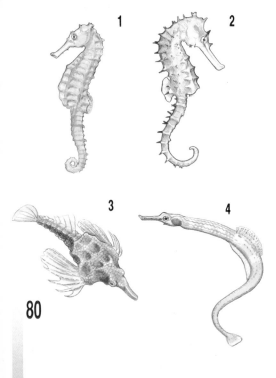

If, in the fish world, there is a fish family which looks unlike what we are used to as a fish body shape, it is the family of Sea Horses and Pipe Fishes, both of which are excellent examples.

Sea Horses **(1)-(2)** are small fishes that can reach 20 cm (6 inches) and live in sea-grass areas of the sea floor. They mimic the bottom background, making it very difficult to see them. When swimming, they have an almost unique vertical advance, using their tail to attach to the sea grass. A very popular and well-loved fish, mentioned among ancient fishes in Greek Mythology as a "symbol of fidelity".

This remarkable family of Sea Horses and Pipe Fishes have a unique reproduction behavior. The female sets the eggs in a pouch located in the stomach area of the male. The male makes the fecundation and gives birth to the young Sea Horses after approximately 45 days.

80

The very small Dragon Fish (Sea Moth) *(3)*, from the same family, is a strange bottom-swimming fish and can be seen in pairs on the sandy floor. Pipe fishes *(4)-(5)*, in different varieties, are elongated and also swim on the sea floor.

The strange and rare Ghost Fish *(6)* is a small fish (5 cm, 2 inches) which also swims vertically in-between the grass on the bottom and also close to black sea urchins between the spines.

The Trumpet Fish *(7)*, a distant relative of the Pipe Fish, is found in the open water close to coral formations, searching for food. (It is a very fast swimmer when catching its prey.) Can reach 1.5 m (5 feet).

THE TRUMPET FISH *(FISTULARIA PETIMBA)*

5

6

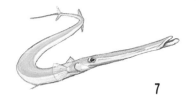

7

81

AN IMPRESSIVE SHORT SPINE PORCUPINE FISH *(CHILOMYCTERUS SPILOSTYLUS)* **LOOKING LIKE A BALLOON**

82

Another group of unusual fishes, named for their ability, when provoked, to expand their bodies by drawing water into the abdomen (or air out of the water), becoming balloon-like.

Puffers are well-known for having a powerful toxin in certain internal organs that can cause serious illness and, in some cases, death from eating this fish.

The Masked *(1)*, the Black Spotted *(2)* and the Bristly *(3)* Puffers are typical of the Red Sea. In some areas common together with the Short Spine Porcupine Fish *(4)*. *(5-6-7)* are Little Puf-

FISHES

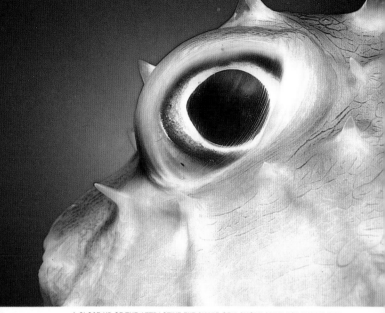

A CLOSE-UP OF THE ATTRACTIVE EYE SHAPE OF A SHORT SPINE PORCUPINE FISH

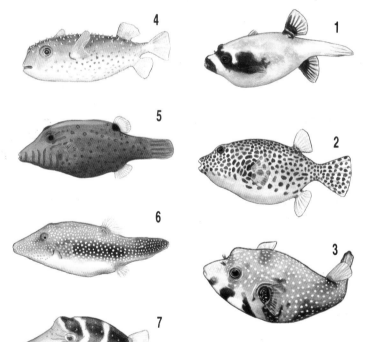

fers reaching only a maximum of 5 cm. They become an attractive show when seen blowing themselves up like balloons. They are relatively friendly and can be touched easily by divers during the blowing up, but it is important to avoid lifting them out of the water as they suck air and this is dangerous for the fish.

BOX FISHES — TRUNK FISHES

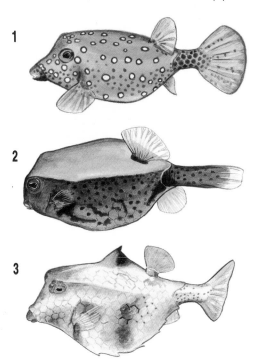

Box Fishes or Trunk Fishes are coral fishes which also have unusual body shapes. Their name comes from the hard external carapace of the different varieties, some of them quadrangular, triangular or pentagonal. These hard carapaces provide adequate protection from most predators, but some species have another defence, a skin poison, that is secreted when the fish is under stress or in danger. They are slow swimmers, propelling themselves by a sculling action of dorsal and anal fins.

·They are very amusing and it is a nice experience to follow them, especially the juveniles, in the reef.

The Spotted Box Fish *(1)* (*(1A)* juvenile) are the most common and the juveniles can be seen mostly in openings of caves, looking like a small cube floating in the water.

THE BLUE SPOTTED BOX FISH *(OSTRACION SP.)* **— FUNNY FISH IN THE REEF**

84

The Blue Spotted Box Fish *(2)* is less common and the Trunk Fish *(3)* can be seen mainly on a sandy bottom.

THE SYMBIOSIS BETWEEN THE CLOWN FISH AND THE SEA ANEMONE IN THE REEF

One of the most interesting and typical symbiotic associations to watch is the Clown Fish (or Anemone Fish) living with the Sea Anemone.

These quite common fish can be seen, when adult, in pairs in close relation to the Anemone. They enjoy protection from the tentacles of the anemone, which are poisonous to other fish, due to the fact that the Clown Fish is immune to the poison of the tentacles, thereby taking advantage of that privilege to hide, when in danger, between them. The females lay their eggs under the anemone to protect them from predators. The eggs can be seen very easily by divers as they appear as big red patches on top of the rock close to the anemone and are usually protected by the male which becomes very aggressive in his protection of them. (Page 75).

The anemone also have their own protection, in the form of the Anemone Fish, which chase away certain fish that are able to eat the tentacles (some varieties of the Butterfly Fish).

Juvenile Clown Fish can be seen in groups in some anemones.

REFLECTION OF CLOWN FISH IN THE MASK

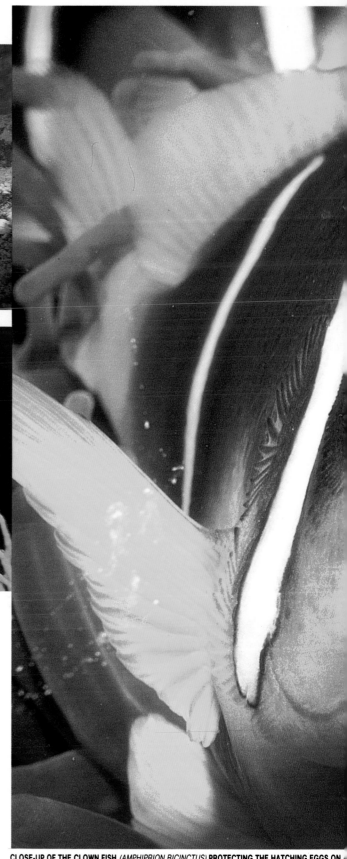

This typical association in the reef is one of the most attractive and interesting subjects for divers, photographers and biologists. They use this example to study the cooperation between animals in the wild who protect and assist each other in feeding and reproduction such as the different varieties of Sea Anemones which host Clown Fish. There is only one species of Anemone Fish in the Red Sea.

CLOSE-UP OF THE CLOWN FISH *(AMPHIPRION BICINCTUS)* PROTECTING THE HATCHING EGGS ON

YELLOW CONTRAST OF AN ANGLER FISH ON RED SPONGE

STRANGE CREATURE IS THE ANGLER FISH

INCREDIBLE CAMOUFLAGE OF AN ANGLER FISH *(ANTENNARIUS SP.)* ON RED SPONGE

An almost perfect camouflage is presented by the Frog Fish. Adapting its colors to the background surroundings makes it very difficult to be discovered by the diver. The same thing occurs with many small fish which, when passing near the Frog Fish without noticing it, are immediately devoured.

The Frog Fish also has a very thin filament with a small ball-like shape in the end above its mouth. The fish moves this filament in circles in order to attract the attention of small fishes. The small prey, curious to see the ball-like, or angler, of the filament (above the mouth), are immediately swallowed up.

The different colours adopted by the fish are directly related to the background colours of the area which they inhabit. The fish are able to change colour slowly in areas of changing colours. This is why it is often very difficult for the diver searching the reef to discover this unusual fish.

ANOTHER STRANGE COLOR CAMOUFLAGE OF THE ANGLER FISH

A BLACK ANGLER FISH ON ALGAE

AN ANGLER FISH READY TO CATCH THE PREY

◄ ◄
A GREEN MIMETIC ANGLER FISH *(ANTENNARIUS SP.)* ON A SPONGE

89

◄
AN ANGLER FROG FISH

THE RED SEA CORAL REEF PARADISE FOR UNDERWATER PHOTOGRAPHY

CORAL REEFS

Submerging ourselves in the shallows under the surface of the water, several meters off shore, we begin to view a breathtaking spectacle exposed in front of our eyes. A fantastic display of colorful forms composes the Coral Reef, together with thousands of colorful fish, some of them described on previous pages of this book. All of these spectacles continue when we descend to the deep blue waters of the Reef, to depths of 70 m or more.

This very rich ecosystem includes millions of sea creatures from microscopic organisms to enormous coral heads and huge fish. This complex creates the Coral Reef, still so unusual to the human eye and attracting the interest to learn more about this unknown underwater world.

The Red Sea is priveleged to have one of the richest variety of coral formations, from fringing reefs close to the shore to submerged islands populated by a colourful combination of soft and stony corals. Amongst them live thousands of creatures from microscopic animals to representatives of the invertebrate kingdom and the coral fish population.

The annual pilgrimage of thousands of divers who come to this area to admire the marvellous tropical sea world is today aspired to by divers all over the world. It is an important mission of all countries involved in this area to preserve the coral reefs from destruction

DRAMATIC DROP-OFF OF THE REEF

STONY CORALS

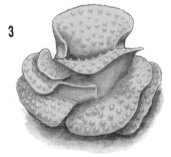

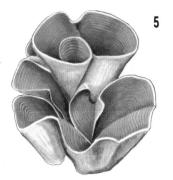

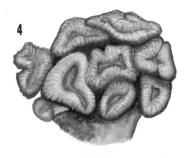

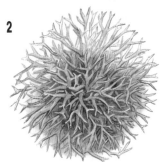

The Invertebrates (spineless) include a large variety of sea animals, among them all the types of Corals, Sponges, Anemones, Crabs, Shrimps, Lobsters, Sea Stars, Sea Urchins, Sea Cucumbers, Feather Stars, all Molluscs (snails, shells, nudibranches, octopus, squid), all types of sea worms, etc. Some representatives of these invertebrates have been selected to be presented in this book.

THE CORALS

In the different groups of corals, the Stony Corals are the creatures mainly responsible for the Reef formation. Secreting calcareous materials, these, together with other organisms, build the enormous Reef wall formations. From the more than 150 varieties of Stony Corals, we mention in this chapter only some of the best known species found all over the Reefs.

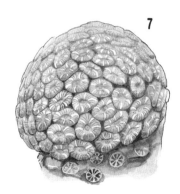

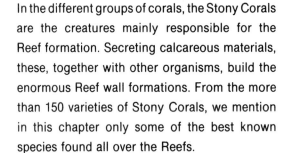

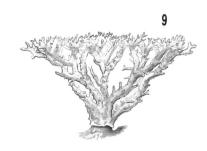

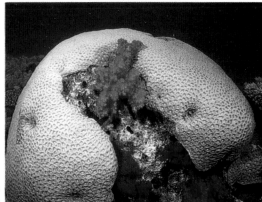

**DIFFERENT COLORS CONTRAST
BETWEEN CORALS IN THE REEF**

AN IMPRESSIVE BLACK CORAL TREE *(ANTHIPATARIA)* **IN DEEP WATER**

A very interesting type of coral closely related to the Stony Coral is the Black Coral.

Black Corals are found only in deeper waters and the name is derived from the very dark color of the skeleton of these creatures. This skeleton is very hard and today is very desirable for use in making jewelry.

In nature, only scuba divers can have the experience of actually seeing the attractive formations of tree or cable-like (Whip Corals) Black Coral.

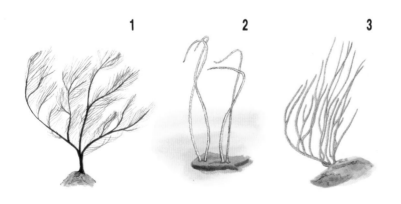

SOFT **C**ORALS — **G**ORGONIANS

AMAZING COLOR COMBINATION OF SOFT CORALS *(SCLERONEPTHTIA SP.)* AND SPONGES IN THE REEF

COLORFUL SOFT CORALS *(DENDRONEPHTYA)* (RED) AND LYTOPHITON (YELLOW)
UNDER A TABLE CORAL

This group of Corals is an important part of the landscape in the Coral Reef. Most of them look like soft plants and do not secrete calcarean skeleton, which means that they are not part of the reef builders. With the exception of the Pipe Organ Coral which has an interesting hard red skeleton, and the different delicate Gorgonians which also have a relatively hard skeleton, many look like sea fans.

Soft Corals are very colorful and play an important role in the general appearance and coloration of the Coral Reefs. Many varieties can be found, some open and exposed to sunlight and others in the shade or inside caves. Only a few representatives of these beautiful creatures are included in this chapter.

95

SEA **A**NEMONES

Like flowers in the sea, the Sea Anemones are animals closely related to the corals.

Living mostly among the coral formations and at various depths, they also add a significant visual enchantment to the variability of the Reef population.

Sea Anemones are usually individual animals (most of the corals are colonies) and some species live in large clusters. They have a soft body with a mouth surrounded by tentacles, some of them with a potent sting. Quantities of these stinging cells erupt when disturbed or touched and are paralyzing to the prey, usually small fish or crabs, which are brought to the mouth to be digested.

96

THE ROSE ANEMONE *(CERIANTHUS)*

S PONGES

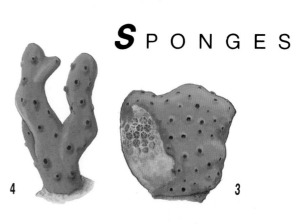

4   3

THE RED SPONGE *(LATRANCULIA SP.)* **WITH THE NUDIBRANCHES** *(GLOSODORIS CUADRICOLOR)* **(4)**

Another important component of the variability of forms and colors in the reef, Sponges are very simple and primitive creatures in their body structure.

Sponges lack a defined nervous system and muscular tissue. They feed on microscopic organisms that float in the water by pumping them in and out of a filtering mechanism in their body.

Many Sponges are brightly colored, living in different areas of the Coral Reef at various depths.

97

THE PIPE SPONGE AND RED SPONGE ADDING BEAUTY TO THE REEF (1)

1

CLOSE-UP OF A BIG CORAL CRAB IN THE REEF AT NIGHT

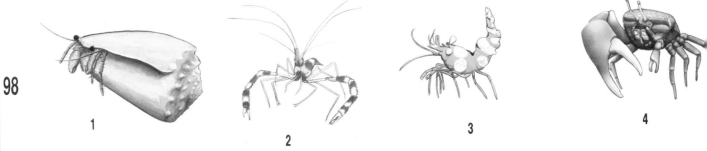

1

2

3

4

HERMIT CRABS IN SYMBIOTIC LIFE WITH ANEMONES ON TOP OF THE SHELL

Many thousands of different varieties of Crustaceans exist in the living population of the sea waters. These range from the microscopic ones which are part of the plankton (microscopic life) floating and moving with the currents and comprising an important component of the food chain in marine life, to others reaching giant sizes, such as crabs, lobsters, etc.

Most of the Reef Crustaceans are nocturnal, hiding during the day and actively searching for food during the night. Some display very interesting behavior, such as Hermit Crabs — hiding its soft abdomen inside an empty shell; Banded Coral Shrimp — typical cleaner of parasites of the reef fishes; Lobsters — hiding by day in deep caves and walking on the reef table, with its impressive appearance, searching for food; Sand Beach Crab — building deep holes in the beach to hide in when in danger; and many others with their own unique behavior.

5

6

A large variety of representatives in the Invertebrate (without backbone) Kingdom are the Marine Molluscs, from the Sea Snails, common to rare species, the Shells, from the Giant Clam (reaching 60 cm in our area) to the other small and colorful ones. The strange Nudibranches are without shells and have exposed gills like incredible flowers on a colorful body background.

Possessing perhaps the most intelligent brain among all of the invertebrates are the Octopus and the Squid, fast moving or swimming Molluscs, which always attract the attention of humans.

All of the Molluscs add an important quantitative component to the marine life population.

A GIANT AND BEAUTIFUL SEA SNAIL — THE TRITON (CHARONIA TRITONIS)

THE WELL-KNOWN OCTOPUS (OCTOPUS VULGARIS) **PHOTOGRAPHED AT NIGHT**

A GIANT NUDIBRANCH — THE SPANISH DANCER *(HEXABRANCHUS SANGUINEUS)*

DIVERS WATCHING A NUDIBRANCH *(GLOSODORIS SP.)*

OPEN LIMA CLAM *(LIMA SP.)* WITH TENTACLES

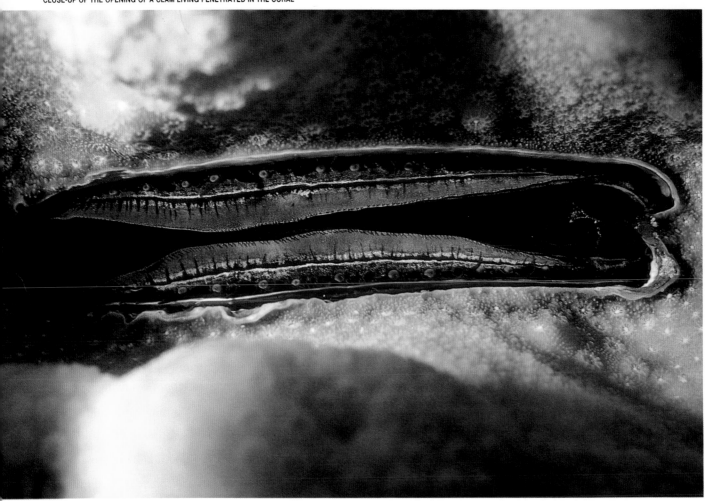

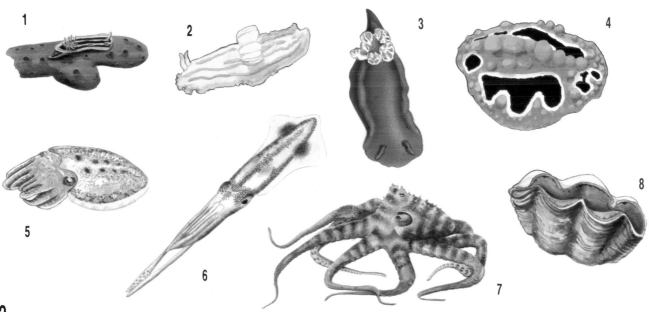

1

2

3

4

5

6

7

8

MAGNIFICENT FEATHER STAR PHOTOGRAPHED AT NIGHT *(CRINOIDEA)*

Another fascinating group of the marine life is the Echinoderms. This group includes a large variety of families with many varied shapes, behaviors and colors, all adding an important influence on the food chain process in the Coral Reefs, either as prey or predators of other organisms.

The Sea Stars, or Starfishes, mostly with five main arms, are predators of shells and also of living corals (such as the Crown of Thorns). The numerous varieties of Sea Urchin species include the spiny and painful (when touched) reef urchin or the capriciously designed sand urchins (sand dollars). The night's flower gardens of Feather Stars have colorful erected arms extended to catch microscopic food. Among the inhabitants of the sea bottom are the Sea Cucumbers with their long, sluggish and relatively soft bodies, extracting organic food from the sand.

BEAUTIFUL SEA LILY OR FEATHER STAR ON THE REEF *(CRINOIDEA)*

1

2

3

5

6

4

7

8

9

10

11

This whole group also becomes an important characteristic of the Coral Reefs and surrounding area.

ARTISTIC PHOTO OF A FEATHER STAR

FEATHER WORMS

The Feather Worms are also a fascinating group of animals which look like beautiful and colorful flowers, when they are actually the tentacles of a worm living in tubes. When the tentacles sense danger, they disappear into the worm tube with incredible speed.

A COMMON FEATHER WORM *(SABELASTARTEN SP.)* **WITH EXPOSED TENTACLES**

LIKE FLOWERS IN THE REEF, FEATHER WORMS ARE OFTEN SEEN BETWEEN CORALS

INCREDIBLE VARIETY OF COLORS IN THE FEATHER DUSTERS

ALGAE AND PLANTS

Important marine life, closely related to the ecosystem of the neighborhood of Coral Reefs, is found on the sandy sea floor, especially in the shallows where an important population of sea plants extends between empty areas of reef.

Among these plants and algae (Palm Plant, Sea Grass, Caulerpa), an incredible and numerous small marine life exists, feeding or finding shelter among the grass.

In previous descriptions of fishes and invertebrates, we mentioned some of the organisms living in grassy areas.

LIKE A SMALL PALM, THE PALM GRASS *(THALASSIA SP.)* ADDS BIG GREEN BEDS TO THE SEA FLOOR

SEA GRASS *(THALASSIA SP.)* IS A COMMON SEA PLANT ON SANDY BOTTOMS

SEA TURTLES

In our area, we can find several varieties of these marine reptiles — sea turtles are air-breathers, but are submerged most of the time.

In order to reproduce, females lay eggs in nests deep in the sand on the seashore and, after hatching (60 days), the offspring return to the sea. Green turtles and hawksbill turtles are the most common in our area. Green turtles are sea grass feeders and can reach huge sizes (6 feet, 1.80 meters) and close to 300 kilograms in weight. Hawksbill turtles feed mostly on fish and jellyfish and reach sizes of up to 60 cm. (2 ft) and 30 kg in weight. This attractive and peaceful creature is often seen by divers who can approach them quite easily.

Today, sea turtles are protected in many areas of the world, following generations of over-fishing, which endangered all of the sea turtle populations in the sea.

A HAWKSBILL TURTLE SWIMMING IN OPEN WATERS

Numerous marine organisms are considered dangerous to humans. To be aware of the existence of these animals and to know how to avoid them assure a safe relationship between us and these animals. There are approximately 1000 species of marine vertebrates, such as fish and many more invertebrates, including corals, urchins, jellyfishes, and snails that are known as venomous or poisonous. They use these properties or mechanisms mainly to protect themselves from enemies and not for attacking.

Venomous animals are those which are capable of producing a poison in a gland or group of cells and can deliver this toxin while biting or stinging.

Poisonous animals are those whose tissues are either in part or entirely toxic to eat.

The Red Sea, like other tropical seas, has a large variety of animals which could be dangerous to man. It is important for those involved in swimming, diving, fishing or any other activity that puts them in contact with marine animals, to be aware and know the most common and important dangerous animals. Many of these are described in other parts of this book.

Over the last few decades, scientists have been working on studies of the behaviour of these organisms, ways to avoid danger, and the different medical treatments in case of injury.

These animals can be divided into three major groups:

(1) Those that *BITE, CUT* OR *SLASH*, like sharks, barracuda, moray eels, surgeonfish and others,

(2) Those that are *VENOMOUS*, like scorpion-fish, sting-rays, sea urchins and others and

(3) Those that are *POISONOUS* TO EAT, such as different species of pufferfish.

This division is not absolute, meaning that animals that *bite or cut can also inject venom.*

SEVERAL VARIETIES OF SHARKS ARE POTENTIALLY DANGEROUS.

PUFFER FISHES ARE POISONOUS TO EAT.

We will, in this chapter, cover only the most common animals existing in this area and those most frequently encountered.

The important points to know about these animals are their *identification*, their *habitat*, the *symptoms* of the injury they inflict and basic medical *treatment*.

IDENTIFICATION

It is important to know how to identify the animal and, if possible, the species. Different species have different effects.

HABITAT

Knowing the animal and its habitat can help us to predict which animals we may encounter, as well as to avoid the danger. For example, many animals hide under the sand in shallow areas, therefore it is advisable to *wear shoes when wading in the shallows*.

SYMPTOMS

When we are able to identify the symptoms of an injured person, we can better determine the type of first-aid necessary.

TREATMENT

Familiarizing ourselves with the expected symptoms can also contribute important information in case further medical treatment is required.

FIRE CORALS, VERY COMMON IN SHALLOWS, STING WHEN TOUCHED.

LEMONSHARK, FOUND IN ALL TROPICAL SEAS, IS ONE OF THE MOST POTENTIALLY DANGEROUS.

There are many marine creatures that can cause physical injury or trauma which can lead to a range of complications. We will mention here some of the animals that are common in the Red Sea.

SHARKS
There are several species of potentially dangerous sharks, especially if they are provoked or excited by food, for example, the tiger shark, mako shark, oceanic white-tip, hammerhead shark, or gray reef shark. Sharks can attack humans for different reasons; spearfishing can be such a trigger, exciting the shark where wounded or bleeding fish become a stimulus for the shark to eat. Swimming or jumping from boats in open water can attract sharks in the vicinity while also appealing to their feeding instincts. When there are sharks in the area, divers and swimmers should move slowly and stay close to reef walls or coral heads while keeping track of the shark's behaviour. Swimmers are advised to leave the water when there are sharks in the area.

BARRACUDAS
This fish, described on page 31, is also considered potentially dangerous. It would be safe to behave around barracudas as one would in the company of sharks.

MORAY EELS

Normally considered a harmless fish, the moray can bite when it feels threatened or is provoked with food. The bite can be serious and can inflict deep wounds; some species are thought to have a mucus in their canine teeth which can cause complications and slow the healing process.

Other animals, such as the *SURGEONFISH,* refers to page 39-40, are completely non-aggressive, but do have a defence mechanism which can cause inadvertent injury when handled. These animals are usually too agile to be caught, but can be approached at night when they are asleep. *AS A GENERAL RULE FOR OUR OWN AND FOR THE ANIMAL'S SAFETY WE SHOULD AVOID TOUCHING ANY ANIMAL.*

FIRST-AID TREATMENT

All physical injuries from marine life should be washed with antiseptic solution and covered as soon as possible. Serious injuries and profuse bleeding should be given professional medical treatment.

MORAY EEL SHOWING HIS TEETH FOR DEFENCE.

113

STINGING, VENOMOUS ANIMALS: FISH

There is a large group of fish and invertebrates that have sting and venom which can cause serious injury or even death. Such animals include: scorpionfish, stingrays, sea urchins, anemones, mollusks, jellyfish and corals. As a general rule, these are all non-aggressive creatures and injury occurs when humans, inadvertently or not, touch them. Again, in this chapter, we will deal with only the most common or dangerous of these animals.

The common characteristic of these animals is the method of inflicting injury by introducing venom through the skin by a stinging mechanism. The spine of a stingray can be 20 cm long, while the stinging mechanism of a fire coral is microscopic, demonstrating the diversity of this weapon.

THE COMMON LIONFISH (PTEROIS VOLITANS) STINGS PEOPLE WHO TOUCH IT

A SCORPIONFISH (SCORPAENOPSIS BARBATA) HAS PERFECT CAMOUFLAGE WITH ITS BACKGROUND

STINGING FISHES

SCORPIONFISHES / STONEFISHES / LIONFISHES

The most infamous of this category is the family of scorpionfish, including the stonefish and the lionfish, referred to in this book on pages 58 - 60 As a group, they rely on camouflage and a sedentary lifestyle for hunting and protection. Knowing that, it is easy to understand why they are often found among corals and between stones in shallow waters.This fact makes them especially dangerous to scuba divers and swimmers who frequently touch them, mistaking them for corals or rocks.

The venom of this group of fish is located in numerous spines found in the dorsal, anal and pectoral fins. The venom gland of the stonefish is activated by pressure on the spine itself, causing it to inject the poison into the victim, resulting in severe pain as the first symptom. The effects of the sting inflicted by the lionfish are particularly painful and that of the stonefish can be life-threatening.

114

THE TELESCOPIC STONEFISH (INIMICUS FILAMENTOSUS) IS MOSTLY FOUND BURIED IN THE SAND

RABBITFISH *(SIGANUS STELLATUS)* **PAIRING IN THE REEF**

STINGRAYS

This group of fish, referred to on page 27 - 29, is related to sharks and is considered very dangerous. Unlike their relatives, they don't bite, but have one or more spines at the base of their tail. This grooved spine is covered with a poisonous mucus which, when penetrated through the skin, leaks into the wound. Part of the spine often breaks off in the wound and continues to leak its venom. It is typical for the stingray to hide under a layer of sand when resting, frequently in very shallow waters, making it risky to wade or rest on the sea floor when scuba diving.

RABBIT FISHES

This family of edible fishes is common in schools in shallow, sandy areas and lagoons. They are in great demand as they are very tasty. The spines of the rabbitfish are covered with a mucus that cause pain and discomfort when penetrated through the skin. All of the spines are painful, but it is especially the first of the dorsal spines, which is aimed forward, of which one must beware.

FIRST-AID TREATMENT

Common to all of the above fish, the poison is a protein which is broken down by heat, therefore the first step of the first-aid should be immersion of the injured part into water that is as hot as can be endured. This should be done for at least 15-20 minutes and, if that does not give relief, should be repeated. The application of vinegar or ammonia also gives good results. The victim should be calmed down and moved slowly, if necessary, to avoid rapid spread of the venom through the body. If the symptoms persist, medical attention should be sought while first-aid is being administered. Anti-venom for certain types of these poisons can be found in some hospitals.

115

INVERTEBRATES

FIRE CORALS *(MILLEPORA SP.)* CAUSE PAINFUL STINGS AND SKIN COMPLICATIONS

A large variety of marine invertebrates are considered dangerous to man. As they are too numerous to mention them all, some examples are described here.

This group of corals, sea anemones, jellyfishes and hydroids has a very interesting stinging mechanism - when they are disturbed by contact they discharge thousands of tiny, poisonous spears, so tiny that they are visible only under a microscope. These spears are produced in cells called nematocysts and are covered with a venom that can cause serious pain, allergic reaction and superficial wounds. Other complications, such as infections, inflammation, fever and nausea are not unusual.

FIRE CORAL
This coral is common in shallow waters of the coral reef. It is responsible for many injuries to swimmers, snorkelers and scuba divers.

TRUE CORAL
Some species of stony and soft corals can incur injuries, such as cuts, allergic reactions and wounds that are easily infected in sea water conditions.

STONY CORALS *(POCILLOPORA SP.)* WITH SHARP SKELETONS
THAT CAN CAUSE WOUNDS AND SKIN INFECTIONS

SEA ANEMONES
Most of the common anemones on the coral reef are more or less harmless. Only a few, such as the small Triactis anemone that lives in colonies on the reef, can inflict painful stings when touched. Complications such as fever, infections and neurological symptoms can occur.

TENTACLED SEA ANEMONE *(TRIACTIS PRODUCTA)* ARE VERY
PAINFUL TO TOUCH AND CAN CAUSE
SERIOUS COMPLICATIONS

HARMLESS-LOOKING SEA PLUMES PRODUCE SERIOUS ALLERGIC REACTIONS TO THE SKIN

SEA PLUMES

Contact with sea plumes can cause serious pain and strong allergic reactions.

JELLYFISHES

The Red Sea is free of the more dangerous types of jellyfishes, however, a number of micro-planktonic jellyfishes are found in the open waters. They appear in great numbers during some seasons of the year and cause stinging and itching to the skin of the victim.

The upside-down jellyfish, Cassiopea, that lives on sandy bottoms, can inflict unpleasant stings when disturbed.

BLACK SEA URCHIN, VERY COMMON IN THE REEFS, CAUSES PAINFUL STINGS

SEA URCHINS

The common black sea urchin, abundant in the shallows, is one of the most well-known causes of injuries to swimmers and bathers. When touched or stepped on, their spines penetrate the skin, causing damage that varies according to the amount of spines, the depth of the penetration and the part of the body affected. No attempts should be made to remove the spines - they are dissolved by the body and attempts to remove them will result in wounds that are easily infected. The red urchin, Asthenosoma, that lives in deeper areas of the reef, has small, but very venomous spines. Scuba divers, tempted to touch this very attractive urchin, are stung, experiencing a strong, burning pain.

STINGS FROM THE RED URCHIN, IN DEEPER REEFS, ARE
VERY PAINFUL AND AFFECT MAINLY SCUBA DIVERS

117

Sea Stars

The Crown of Thorns, a spiny sea star, is not often seen in the Red Sea. When touched, a throbbing pain results.

CROWN OF THORNS (ACANTHASTER PLANCI) SEA STAR HAS SPINES PAINFUL TO THE TOUCH

FIRST-AID TREATMENT
Injuries from all of the group of invertebrates should be treated by applying an antiseptic to prevent infection. Antihistamine creams, vinegar or ammonia can also be applied to the wound to relieve the pain. In severe cases, seek medical attention as soon as possible.

Mollusks

There are some 400 species of cone shells in the tropical seas. All have a well-developed venom apparatus. Only a few of those found in the Red Sea, however, can be considered dangerous to humans.

This shell inhabits shallow waters close to reefs and sandy bottoms. The animal has a siphon tube containing a long spine that can shoot out and inject a strong venom. This spine is normally used to paralyze the prey, usually small fish that the cone shell feeds on. Humans who accidentally handle the shell can be seriously injured by the toxin which closely resembles snake venom. Symptoms vary from weak to very strong pain. The affected area can become swollen with a bluish ring around the wound. These symptoms can develop into severe numbness, partial or total paralysis and respiration difficulties.

FIRST-AID TREATMENT
Apply a pressure bandage to avoid blood circulation in the affected area. Make the patient rest and get urgent medical assistance.

CONE (CONUS SP.) IS CONSIDERED VERY DANGEROUS

POISONOUS FISH

All members of the puffer fish family are poisonous to eat, as described on page 82-83. This fish should not be eaten under any circumstances. It contains a highly potent toxin (tetrodotoxin), located mainly in the skin and internal organs, such as the liver and intestines. Only the musculature area is free of poison and may be eaten. In Japan, there are special restaurants called "fugu" fish restaurants where specialist cooks prepare unique and expensive dishes with this fish. There have been no cases of poisoning reported from this type of fish in our area.

FIRST-AID TREATMENT
In case of accidental ingestion of this fish, induce vomiting and seek medical assistance urgently.

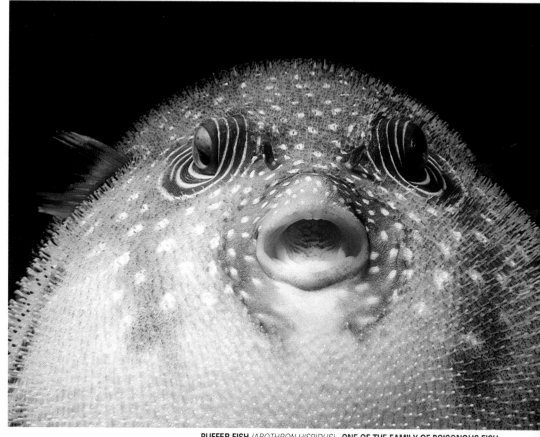

PUFFER FISH *(AROTHRON HISPIDUS)* - ONE OF THE FAMILY OF POISONOUS FISH

CIGUATERA - FISH POISONING
There are several types of large predator fish, usually found in the reefs in tropical areas, which may be toxic to humans. This happens due to the predator fish feeding on small herbivorous fish which may have eaten an algae toxic to man. Groupers, barracudas, big snappers, morays and other predators can carry this toxin. These edible fishes, favourites of many people, can be dangerous to eat in some tropical areas, mainly the Caribbean, the South Pacific and Australia. There have not been any reports of poisoning of this type in our area.

FIRST-AID TREATMENT
The treatment described with regard to puffer fish poisoning is applicable in this case as well.

PREDATORS LIKE GROUPERS ARE POTENTIALLY POISONOUS

119

CORAL WORLD, EILAT

Underwater Observatory and Aquarium

Many of the wonders included in this book can be seen on display at the **Coral World, Eilat** underwater observation tower or in the different tanks, pools and aquariums.

Coral World is situated 5 miles (7 kilometers) south of the town of Eilat in the Coral Beach Nature Reserve.

It took four years of expert biological research, planning and building to open the gates to visitors in March 1975. In this first stage of Coral World, the exhibits consisted of an underwater observatory and an aquarium with small tanks displaying the small marine life. In 1982 a huge circular reef tank (replica of the Red Sea Coral Reef) was added,

displaying six schools of different coral fish that are not seen from the underwater observatory, and three big pools for sharks, rays, sea turtles and other big creatures. This large circular tank and the pools enabled the display of other marine creatures of our area: schooling fish that are not visible from the tower, giant sea turtles and stingrays, and a rich variety of deep and shallow water sharks. All can be observed through big panoramic windows or from the boardwalk above. All these displays of aquariums, tanks and pools are operated by a natural seawater flow "open system." Water is pumped directly from the sea and flows without any filtration into the aquariums circulating 24 hours a day, all year round.

An aerial view of Coral World, Eilat

This system allows a huge variety of delicate corals and other invertebrates to be kept in captivity together with colorful fish that make this display the richest "Red Sea" exhibit in the world.

The first underwater observatory (1975) became too small to receive the huge amount of visitors that come yearly to look at the "Red Sea Wonders" 5 meters deep through its windows. In 1991 a new and modern underwater observatory tower with big panoramic acrylic windows was connected to the old one by an underwater tunnel. Both observatories are unique in the world allowing observation of an important part of the local coral reef formations and huge variety of fish surrounding this habitat in the open sea. The new tower also has an aerial observation deck 25 meters high where the visitor can observe a breathtaking view and an encounter with four nations' borders (Israel-Jordan-Egypt-Saudi Arabia).

Right: **The sea turtle pool**
Below: **The aquarium's unique sea life display**
Opposite:
Above: **A window in the Shark Pool**
Below: **Panoramic windows of the circular reef tank**

One of the aquarium windows

The transplantation of living coral heads around the towers has created a new habitat and territory for the thousands of marine creatures which today form a permanent population around the reef. Visitors can observe the fish which are free to stay or leave.

The observatories are connected to the shore by a 300 feet (100 meters) bridge 10 feet (3 meters) above the water surface.

All these installations in the sea involved expert biological, technical and engineering studies and planning.

Displayed in all its glory in the aquarium are species of Red Sea life that will amaze the visitor. The completely natural colors and balanced interactions between coral fishes and invertebrates in 25 aquarium of various sizes inside two geodesic domes with a comfortable air-conditioned temperature can be observed in hundreds of colorful and interesting fish and living corals, sea anemones and other unique sea creatures.

A remarkable display is the dark room with a unique exhibit of flashlight fish which, with their luminescent organs, illuminate the completely dark room. Another incredible display is the fluorescence in living corals where the amazing colors of these creatures can be seen glowing under U.V. (blacklight).

Coral World affords the visitor a unique opportunity to get acquainted with the splendour of underwater life in the Red Sea. It also operates a modern 48-passenger submarine that takes visitors to a depth of 200 feet (60 meters), enabling them to enjoy in a novel way the fantastic reef formations and thousands of colorful fish, typical of the wonders of the Red Sea.

Coral World has a series of stores for souvenirs and photo supplies. There is also a snack bar and restaurant in the facility to make the visitor's stay at the site more enjoyable.